Author

Philippa Gardom-Hulme

THE UNIVERSITY *of York*

OCR
RECOGNISING ACHIEVEMENT

OXFORD
UNIVERSITY PRESS

Official Publisher Partnership

OXFORD
UNIVERSITY PRESS

Great Clarendon Street, Oxford OX2 6DP

Oxford University Press is a department of the University of Oxford.
It furthers the University's objective of excellence in research,
scholarship, and education by publishing worldwide in

Oxford   New York

Auckland   Cape Town   Dar es Salaam   Hong Kong   Karachi
Kuala Lumpur   Madrid   Melbourne   Mexico City   Nairobi
New Delhi   Shanghai   Taipei   Toronto

With offices in
Argentina   Austria   Brazil   Chile   Czech Republic   France   Greece
Guatemala   Hungary   Italy   Japan   Poland   Portugal   Singapore
South Korea   Switzerland   Thailand   Turkey   Ukraine   Vietnam

Oxford is a registered trade mark of Oxford University Press
in the UK and in certain other countries.

British Library Cataloguing in Publication Data.

Data available.

ISBN 978-0-19-913817-3
10 9 8 7 6 5 4 3 2 1

Printed in Great Britain by Bell and Bain Ltd, Glasgow.

Paper used in the production of this book is a natural, recyclable product
made from wood grown in sustainable forests. The manufacturing process
conforms to the environmental regulations of the country of origin.

Acknowledgements
Illustrations by IFA Design, Plymouth, UK, Clive Goodyer, and Q2A Media.

Author acknowledgments
Many thanks to Catherine and Sarah for checking the puzzles, and to Barney
for his inspirational ideas. Thanks to Ruth for her careful editing, and to Les,
Sophie, and Barry at OUP for all their help and patience.

Contents

About this book

Welcome to the Twenty First Century Science Revision Guide!

This book will help you prepare for all your GCSE Core Science module tests. There is one section for each of the biology, chemistry, and physics modules B1 to P3, as well as six sections covering Ideas About Science. Each section includes several types of page to help you revise.

Workout

These help you find out what you can remember already, and get you thinking about the topic. They include puzzles, flow charts, and lots of other types of question. Work through these on your own or with a friend, and write your answers in the book. If you get stuck, look in the Factbank. The index will help you find what you need. Check your answers in the back of the book.

Factbank

The Factbanks summarise information from the module. For B1 to P3, the Factbanks are divided into short sections, each linked to different statements in the specification. The Ideas About Science Factbanks are different. They are conversations, covering the ideas you will need to apply in different contexts. Read them aloud with a friend if you want.

Quickfire

Sections B1 to P3 each have one page of Quickfire questions. These are short questions that cover most of the content of the module. For some questions, there is space to answer in the book. For others, you will need to use paper or an exercise book.

GCSE-style questions

These are like the questions in the module tests. You could work through them using the Factbank to check things as you go, or do them under test conditions. The answers are in the back of the book. Most sections have one six-mark question, designed to test your ability to organise ideas and write in clear and correct English. In modules with significant Higher-tier content, there is a question under the heading 'Going for the highest grades'. These questions test your knowledge and understanding of Higher-tier content, and provide opportunities to practise answering questions at A/A* standard.

Ⓗ In every section, content covered at Higher tier only is shown like this.

Other help

The pages at the front of this book include vital revision tips, hints to help you work out what questions are telling you to do, and help with graphs. Don't skip these!

How to revise

Making the most of revision

You probably won't remember much if you just read this book, or put it under your pillow at bedtime.

Here are some suggestions to help you revise effectively.

Plan your time

Work out how many days there are before your test – then make a timetable so you know which topics to revise and when. Include some time off, to give your brain a rest.

Revise actively

Don't just read the Factbanks. Highlight key points, scribble extra details in the margin or on sticky notes, and make up ways to help you remember things. The messier the Factbanks are by the time you take your test, the better!

Try making **mind maps** to summarise the information in a Factbank, and to link its main points. Start with an important idea in the middle. Use arrows to link this to key facts, examples, and other science ideas.

Test yourself on key facts and ideas. Use the Quickfire sections in this book, or get a friend to ask you questions. You could make revision cards, too. Write a question on one side, and the answer on the other. Then test yourself.

Try making up songs or rhymes to help you remember things. You could make up **mnemonics**, too, like this one for the different types of electromagnetic radiation:

Revising **M**ight **I**mprove **V**icky's **U**nderstanding of **X**-rays and **G**amma rays.

Don't forget you will need to **apply your knowledge** in different contexts, and evaluate data and opinions. The GCSE-style questions in this book give lots of opportunities to practise these skills. Your teacher may give you past test papers, too.

Don't ignore the **Ideas About Science** sections. These are vital. In your module tests, there could be questions on any of the Ideas About Science you have covered so far, set in the context of any of the topics you have covered.

Take plenty of **short breaks** during revision – about 10 minutes per hour works for most people. It's best not to sit still and relax in your breaks – go for a walk, or do some sport. You'll be surprised at what you can remember when you come back to your books, and at how much fresher your brain feels!

Understanding exam questions

Command words

Exam questions use command words to tell you what to do. Make sure you know what they all mean.

Calculate   Work out a number. Use your calculator if you like. You may need to use an equation.

Compare   Write about the ways in which two things are the same, and how they are different.

Describe   Write a detailed answer that covers what happens, when it happens, and where it happens. Your answer must include facts, or characteristics.

Discuss   Write about the issues linked to a topic. You may need to give arguments for and against something, or show the difference between ideas, opinions, and facts.

Estimate   Suggest a rough value, without doing a complete calculation. Use your science knowledge to suggest a sensible answer.

Explain   Write a detailed answer that says how and why things happen. Give mechanisms and reasons.

Evaluate   You will be given some facts, data, or an article. Write about these, and give your own conclusion or opinion on them.

Justify   Give some evidence or an explanation to tell the examiner why you gave an answer.

Outline   Give only the key facts. If you're asked to outline a process, make sure you write down the steps in the correct order.

Predict   Look at the data and suggest a sensible value or outcome. Use trends in the data and your science knowledge to help you.

Show   Write down the details, steps, or calculations to show how to get an answer you have been given.

Suggest   Apply something you have learnt to a new context, or to come up with a reasonable answer to the question.

Write down   Give a short answer. There is no need for an argument to support your answer.

Maximise your marks

Answering exam questions

Read the question carefully, and find the command word. Then look carefully at the information in the question, and at any data. How will they help you answer the question? Use the number of answer lines to help you work out how much detail the examiner wants.

Then write your answer. Make it easy for the examiner to read and understand. If a number needs units, don't forget to include them.

Six-mark questions

Follow the steps below to gain the full six marks:
- Work out exactly what the **question** is asking.
- Jot down **key words** to help you answer the question.
- **Organise** the key words. You might need to group them into advantages and disadvantages, or sequence them to describe a series of steps in a process.
- **Write** your answer. Use the organised key words to help.
- **Check** and correct your spelling, punctuation, and grammar.

What does the examiner think?

Here are an examiner's comments on two answers to a question.

The question

In 2011, an earthquake damaged a Japanese nuclear power station. Radioactive materials escaped into the environment. After this, the government of one European country made this decision:

> We will build no more nuclear power stations. In future, we will generate more electricity from a mix of renewable resources.

Outline the arguments for and against this decision.

✎ The quality of written communication will be assessed.

Answer	Examiner's comments
They are right becoz nuclear power is v dangerus and reknewable energy is things like wind power that aren't dangerous, except the niose is terrible and they looks bad!	This answer makes some correct points. However, the points are not well organised and it is not clear which arguments are for and which against. There are mistakes of spelling, grammar, and punctuation. Grade G.
As the Japanese example shows, there are hazards linked to nuclear power stations. Even though the risk of radioactive materials escaping is small, the consequences can be devastating. This is an argument for the decision. Also, building nuclear power stations makes lots of greenhouse CO_2. Another argument for the decision is that renewable energy resources are sustainable. They make little pollution. One renewable source alone may be unreliable, but with a mix they can generate electricity all the time. The arguments against the decision are that nuclear power is a constant, reliable source of electricity. Also, some people are against wind power because the turbines can kill birds. We don't know if renewables can supply enough electricity to meet demand.	This answer is typical of an A/A* grade candidate. The arguments are made clearly and are organised logically. The candidate has referred to risk and sustainability. The spelling, punctuation, and grammar are faultless.

Understanding graphs

In the exam, you might have to plot a graph or draw a chart, then explain what it shows. Exam questions might also give a graph, and ask you to describe and explain what the graph shows.

Read the axes and check the units

These bar charts give data about electricity use and generation in six European countries.

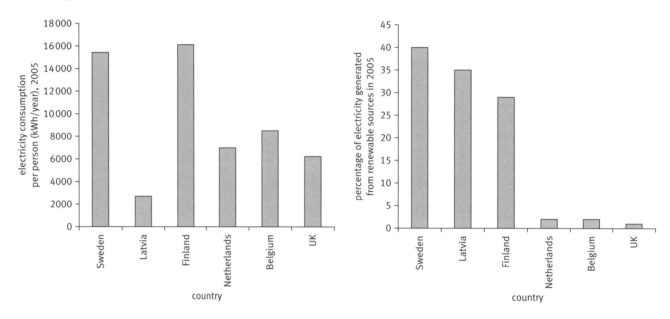

The graphs give data for the same countries, but look very different. One graph shows electricity used per person per year. The other shows the percentage of electricity that is generated from renewable sources.

The graphs illustrate how important it is to **read the axes** and **check the units** when working with graphs.

Describe relationships between variables

The pattern of points on a scatter graph, or the shape of a line graph, shows whether two **factors** are related.

The graph opposite shows a pattern in data on a group of babies born on the same day. As the babies get older, their average head circumference increases.

As the babies get older, the **gradient** gets less steep, or decreases. This shows that the babies' heads are growing more slowly.

The graph on the next page shows how the number of *salmonella* bacteria in a patient's stomach changes over time.

The graph has three phases. If a question asks you to describe the graph, you must describe each phase. Make sure you include data and units in your description.

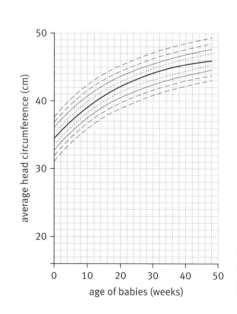

For example:
- The number of bacteria increases rapidly on the first day, until there are about 4.5 million bacteria.
- The number of bacteria stays the same for the next three days, at about 4.5 million.
- During the fourth day, the number of bacteria starts to decrease, until there are fewer than one million bacteria by day six.

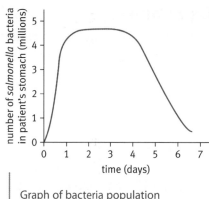

Graph of bacteria population against time.

Is there a correlation?

If one factor changes when another does, the two factors are **correlated**. On the two graphs above, it is easy to see the correlation.

If the two factors are plotted on separate graphs, it is less easy to see if there is a correlation.

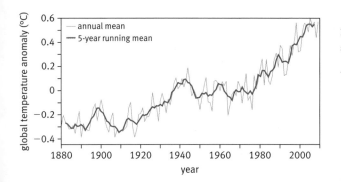
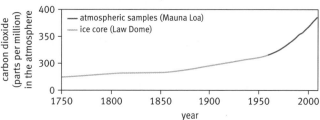

The graphs above show increasing global temperatures and carbon dioxide levels. But they are plotted for different time periods, so it is hard to see if there is a correlation.

If the graphs are plotted on the same set of axes, for the same time period, it is much easier to spot the correlation.

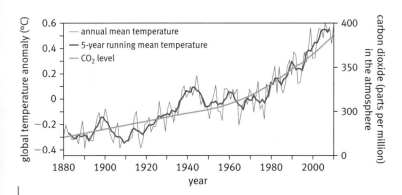

Graph to show the same data as the above two graphs, plotted on one set of axes.

Explaining graphs

A correlation between two factors does not mean that one factor caused the other, although it may have done. Scientists look for a **mechanism** to try to explain why two factors are related.

Equations

You might need to use these equations in the exam. They will be on the exam paper, so you do not need to learn them off by heart.

Module P1 The Earth in the Universe

distance travelled by a wave = wave speed × time

wave speed = frequency × wavelength

Module P3 Sustainable energy

energy transferred = power × time

power = voltage × current

$$\text{efficiency} = \frac{\text{energy usefully transferred}}{\text{total energy supplied}} \times 100\%$$

Units

Length: metres (m), kilometres (km), centimetres (cm), millimetres (mm), micrometres (μm), nanometres (nm)

Mass: kilograms (kg), grams (g), milligrams (mg)

Time: seconds (s), milliseconds (ms), hours (h)

Temperature: degrees Celsius (°C)

Area: cm^2, m^2

Volume: cm^3, dm^3, m^3, litres (l), millilitres (ml)

Speed: m/s, km/s, km/h

Energy: joules (J), kilojoules (kJ), megajoules (MJ), kilowatt-hours (kWh), megawatt-hours (MWh)

Power: watts (W), kilowatts (kW), megawatts (MW)

Frequency: hertz (Hz), kilohertz (kHz)

Information: bytes (B), kilobytes (kB), megabytes (MB)

Useful data

Module C1: proportions of the main gases in the atmosphere: 78% nitrogen, 21% oxygen, 1% argon

Module P1: speed of light = 300 000 km/s

Module P2: electromagnetic spectrum in order of increasing frequency and energy: radio waves, microwaves, infrared, visible light, ultraviolet, X-rays, gamma rays

Module P3: mains supply voltage is 230 V

Chemical formulae for module C1

carbon dioxide CO_2

carbon monoxide CO

sulfur dioxide SO_2

nitrogen monoxide NO

nitrogen dioxide NO_2

water H_2O

1 Use these words to finish labelling the diagram.

cell   nucleus   chromosomes   genes   DNA

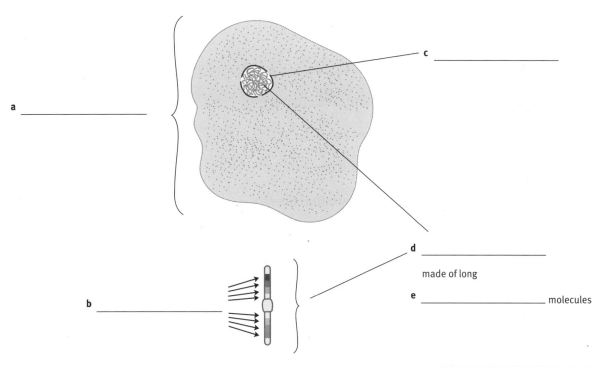

a _____

b _____

c _____

d _____
made of long

e _____ molecules

2 Draw lines to match each characteristic to the factors that determine it.

Characteristics
dimples
weight
eye colour
scars

Factors
genes and environment
one gene only
environment only
several genes working together

Exam tip

Make sure you know what genes, chromosomes, and DNA are.

3 Write the letter **T** next to the statements that are true.

Write the letter **F** next to the statements that are false.

a Women have two X chromosomes in each cell, except for their sex cells. _____

b Men have one Y chromosome in each cell. _____

c Human egg cells contain 46 chromosomes. _____

d Every sperm has an X chromosome. Half of all sperm also have a Y chromosome. _____

e If a sperm with a Y chromosome fertilises an egg, the embryo develops female sex organs. _____

4 Choose words from the box to fill in the gaps.

| clones | genes | unspecialised | environments | asexual | sexual |

Some strawberry plant cells are _____ . These cells

can grow new plants. This is what happens in _____

reproduction. The new strawberry plants have genes that are

exactly the same as their parent's genes. They are _____

of the parent plant. In this case, all the variation between the

strawberry plant and its offspring are caused by differences in

their _____ .

5 For each use of genetic testing listed in the table, write down one
question the person having the test might need to think about.
The first one has been done for you.

Use of genetic testing	Question to think about
For a man to find out if he will develop symptoms of a genetic disorder such as Huntington's disease.	Should I tell my employer if the test result is positive?
a For a pregnant woman to find out if her fetus has two faulty alleles for cystic fibrosis.	
b For a man to find out if he is a carrier of a genetic disorder.	

6 The allele that gives you hair on the middle of your fingers is
dominant (R). The allele for no hair is recessive (r).

a Complete the genetic diagram (Punnett square) for the
mother and father shown.

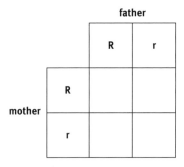

b Use the genetic diagram to help you complete the sentences
below.

i The chance of a child of the mother and father
having hairy fingers is _____ %.

ii The chance of a child of the mother and father not
having hairy fingers is _____ %.

7 Draw a line to link two words on the circle.

Write a sentence on the line saying how the two words are connected.

Repeat for as many words as you can.

chromosome

gene   protein

environment   allele

dominant   recessive

DNA   clones

asexual   sexual

stem cell

B1.1.1–6 What are genes?

Every living organism is made from **cells**. Most cells have a **nucleus**. Inside the nucleus are **chromosomes**. Chromosomes are made from very long molecules of DNA.

Chromosomes contain thousands of **genes**. Genes are instructions that control how a living thing develops and functions. Genes control which proteins a cell makes, including:
- **structural** proteins to build the body, for example collagen
- **functional** proteins to take part in chemical reactions, for example enzymes such as amylase.

Your characteristics depend on your genes and the **environment**.
- Some depend on one gene only, for example dimples.
- Some depend on several genes working together, for example eye colour.
- Some depend on the environment only, for example scars.
- Some depend on genes and the environment, for example weight.

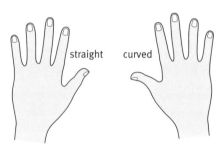

The allele that gives you straight thumbs is dominant. The allele that gives you curved thumbs is recessive.

B1.2.1–6 Why do family members look alike?

Human cells (except sex cells) contain pairs of chromosomes. One chromosome in each pair came from the mother's egg and the other came from the father's sperm.

In the two chromosomes of a pair, the same genes are in the same place. The two genes in a pair can be different. Different versions of the same gene are called **alleles**. For each gene, a person has either two identical alleles or two different alleles.

ℍ If both alleles for a gene are the same, you are **homozygous** for that gene. If both alleles are different, you are **heterozygous**.

You have similarities to your parents because you developed from a fertilised egg that got alleles from your mother and your father.

a father with **Tt** alleles
(straight thumbs)

sex cells	T	t
a mother with **tt** alleles (curved thumbs) t	Tt	tt
t	Tt	tt

There is a 50% chance that a child of these parents will have straight thumbs.

B1.2.7–8, B1.2.12 What makes us different?

Brothers and sisters are not identical. This is because they inherit different combinations of alleles from their parents.

Alleles can be **dominant** or **recessive**. For example, the allele that gives you straight thumbs (**T**) is dominant. The curved thumb allele (**t**) is recessive. If you inherit either one or two dominant alleles (**Tt** or **TT**) you will have straight thumbs. If you inherit two recessive alleles (**tt**) you will have curved thumbs.

ℍ A description of your genes, including your combination of alleles, is called your **genotype**. Your **phenotype** is a description of your characteristics, for example whether or not your thumbs are curved.

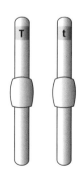

These chromosomes are a pair. The gene controlling thumb shape is shaded. The person inherited one **T** and one **t** allele. He has straight thumbs.

B1.2.9–10 What makes us male or female?

Humans have one pair of sex chromosomes in each body cell. Female humans have two X chromosomes (XX). Males have one X chromosome and one Y chromosome (XY).

The chromosomes in sex cells are not paired up. Every egg has an X chromosome. Half of all sperm have an X chromosome. The other sperm have a Y chromosome.

The Y chromosome includes a sex-determining gene. This makes an embryo develop testes, and so become male. When there is no Y chromosome, the embryo develops ovaries. It is female.

Exam tip

Practise drawing and interpreting genetic diagrams (Punnett squares).

B1.3.1–5 What causes inherited disorders?

Some disorders are caused by inheriting faulty alleles of just one gene.

Huntington's disease develops after age 35. It is fatal.

Symptoms:
- tremor and clumsiness
- memory loss and concentration problems
- mood changes

One faulty dominant allele – **H** – causes Huntington's disease. A person can inherit the disease from just one parent.

a father with **hh** alleles
(does not have
Huntington's disease)

	sex cells	h	h
a mother with **Hh** alleles (does have Huntington's disease)	H	Hh	Hh
	h	hh	hh

There is a 50% chance that a child of these parents will inherit Huntington's disease.

Children with **cystic fibrosis** make thick, sticky mucus. They have:
- difficulty breathing
- difficulty digesting food
- frequent chest infections.

A faulty recessive allele – **f** – causes cystic fibrosis. A child who has two faulty alleles – one from each parent – has cystic fibrosis. A child with one faulty allele is a **carrier**.

Carriers do not have the disorder, but can pass it on to their children.

a father with **Ff** alleles
(carrier of cystic fibrosis)

	sex cells	F	f
a mother with **Ff** alleles (carrier of cystic fibrosis)	F	FF	Ff
	f	Ff	ff

There is a 25% chance that a child of these parents will inherit cystic fibrosis. There is a 50% chance that a child will be a carrier of cystic fibrosis.

B1.3.6–8 Why have genetic tests?

Genetic tests detect faulty alleles.

Reason for test	Issues to consider
For an adult to find out if they are a carrier of a genetic disorder.	Should a carrier have children?
For an adult to find out if they will develop symptoms of a genetic disorder.	Should the adult tell relatives who may also develop symptoms?
For a pregnant woman to find out if her fetus has a genetic disorder.	Should she have an abortion if the test is positive? Will removing cells for the test increase the risk of miscarriage?
To find out how a person might react to a prescription drug.	Should a different drug be used? Does the person need a higher dose?
To find out if embryos created outside the body have faulty alleles, and so choose which to implant in the uterus. This is pre-implantation genetic diagnosis.	Does removing a cell to test damage an embryo? Is it ethically right to destroy embryos with faulty alleles?

The results from genetic tests can be inaccurate. **False positives** wrongly show that a person will develop a disorder. **False negatives** wrongly show that a person will not develop a disorder.

B1.4.1–4 What are clones?

Bacteria, plants, and some animals can reproduce asexually to form clones. **Clones** are individuals with identical genes. Only environmental factors can cause differences between clones.

Plants that produce bulbs or runners are clones of each other. Animals do not usually form clones, but there are exceptions:

- Identical twins are clones. They form when the cells of an embryo separate to make two embryos.
- Scientists make clones by removing an egg cell nucleus. They take a nucleus from an adult body cell of the organism they want to clone, and transfer it to the 'empty' egg cell. They grow the embryo for a few days and implant it into a uterus.

B1.4.5–7 What are stem cells?

Stem cells are unspecialised cells. There are two types.
- **Embryonic stem cells** can develop into any type of cell.
- **Adult stem cells** can develop into many, but not all, types of cell.

Most stem cells become specialised during the early development of a living organism.

Because they are unspecialised, stem cells may be useful in future to treat some illnesses.

Use extra paper to answer these questions if you need to.

1 Choose words from the box to fill in the gaps. Each word may be used once, or not at all.

> **alleles   instructions   proteins   characteristic**
> **carbohydrates   chromosomes   genes   DNA**

Living things are made from cells. Inside every cell nucleus are long threads called _____. These contain thousands of _____. Genes are _____ that control how a living thing will develop. They are codes for making _____. Genes are sections of very long _____ molecules.

2 Highlight the statements below that are **true**. Then write corrected versions of the statements that are **false**.
  a Body cells contain pairs of chromosomes.
  b Different versions of the same gene are called alleles.
  c If a person has one dominant allele in a pair of alleles, they will not show the characteristic linked to that gene.
  d Human male body cells have XX sex chromosomes.
  e A sperm contains pairs of chromosomes.

3 Circle four symptoms of cystic fibrosis from those below.

thick mucus	**tremor**
clumsiness	**difficulty breathing**
chest infections	**memory loss**
digestion problems	**blood in urine**

4 Jess is a carrier of cystic fibrosis. She is pregnant. She is trying to decide whether or not to have a genetic test to find out if her fetus has cystic fibrosis. List three things she might want to consider before having the test.

5 Marfan syndrome is an inherited disorder. It may cause serious heart and eyesight problems. It is caused by faulty alleles (**M**) of a single gene. The faulty allele is dominant.
  a Which of the people listed below will have Marfan syndrome?
    Ellie (**Mm**), Jim (**mm**), Susan (**MM**), Tom (**mM**)
  b Ellie and Jim are having a baby. Draw a Punnett square to work out the chance of the baby having Marfan syndrome.

6 Assume that being able to roll your tongue – or not – is controlled by one pair of alleles. The ability to roll your tongue is dominant (**R**). Not being able to roll your tongue is recessive (**r**).

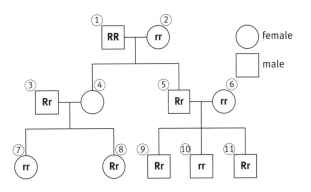

On the family tree above, each person is represented by a number.
  a Write down the pair of alleles that person 4 has.
  b Write the numbers of the people who cannot roll their tongues.
  c Write the numbers of the people who can roll their tongues themselves, but who might have children who cannot roll their tongues.

7 List five symptoms of Huntington's disease.

8 What is a stem cell? Explain the difference between adult and embryonic stem cells.

H 9 Look at the Punnett square below.
  a Use it to help you describe the difference between a person's genotype and their phenotype.
  b Explain how the Punnett square shows that the chance of a baby being female is 50%.

		mother	
		X	**X**
father	**X**	**XX**	**XX**
	Y	**XY**	**XY**

10 Natasha has dimples. Her genotype for dimples is **Dd**.
  a What is Natasha's phenotype for dimples?
  b Is the dimple allele dominant or recessive? Give a reason for your decision.
  c Is Natasha homozygous or heterozygous for dimples? Explain how you know.

11 Explain how the sex-determining gene on the Y chromosome makes an embryo develop into a male.

12 a Explain what is meant by *pre-implantation genetic diagnosis*.
  b Suggest why a man and woman who want a baby may choose to go through this process.
  c Identify the issues the man and woman might need to consider before going through the process.

13 Describe the stages involved in creating an artificial animal clone.

1 Ellen and Hannah are identical twin girls.

a **i** Ellen and Hannah look the same as each other.
Choose the best explanations for this.
Put ticks in the **two** correct boxes.

They have the same combination of alleles. ☐

They inherited genes from both parents. ☐

They both developed from one egg that
was fertilised by one sperm. ☐

Their parents have different
combinationsof alleles. ☐ [1]

ii Ellen and Hannah look different from their mother.
Choose the **wrong** explanation for this.
Put a tick in **one** box below.

A person's characteristics are affected by
both genes and the environment. ☐

They received alleles from both parents. ☐

The twins and their mother have
different combinations of alleles. ☐

Their cells contain 23 pairs of
chromosomes. ☐ [1]

iii Ellen has one pair of sex chromosomes in each
body cell.
Which two chromosomes are in this pair?
Circle the correct answer.

XY   **YY**   **XX** [1]

b **i** John and Jim are identical twins. They are 50 years old.
John is fatter than Jim. Choose the best explanation
for this.
Put a tick in the **one** correct box.

They have different combinations
of alleles. ☐

They are clones of each other. ☐

They have different lifestyles. ☐

John was born an hour before Jim. ☐ [1]

ii John and Jim have stem cells in many of their body
tissues.
What is a stem cell? [1]

iii Suggest one way in which stem cells might be
used in future. [1]

Total [6]

2 The allele that causes straight thumbs is dominant (**T**).
The allele that causes curved thumbs is recessive (t).

Sarah has straight thumbs. She has one **T** allele and
one t allele.
Alan has curved thumbs. He has **tt** alleles.

a **i** What percentage of Sarah's egg cells contain the
allele **T**?

_____ [1]

ii Give the number of **t** alleles in each of Alan's body
cells (*not* the number in his sperm cells).

_____ [1]

b **i** Finish the punnett square to show which alleles
Sarah and Alan's children may inherit.   [3]

ii Sarah and Alan have a baby boy.
What is the chance of his having a straight thumb?
Put a ring round the correct answer.

25%   **50%**   **75%**   **100%**   [1]

Total [6]

		Sarah (mother) Tt	
	sex cells	T	t
Alan (father) tt	t		
	t		

3 Huntington's disease is an inherited disease.
Its symptoms usually develop after the age of 35.

a Give two symptoms of Huntington's disease.

_____ [2]

b Huntington's disease is caused by a dominant allele of
just one gene. The table shows the alleles of this gene in
the cells of four people.

Who will develop Huntington's disease?
Circle the correct name or names.

Abigail   **Brenda**   **Chris**   **Deepa**   [1]

Name	Alleles
Abigail	Hh
Brenda	HH
Chris	hh
Deepa	hh

c Gary is 20. He had a genetic test. The test shows that he
will develop Huntington's disease.

Gary's wife is six weeks pregnant. Suggest one reason why
the couple may decide to test the fetus for Huntington's
disease. Suggest one reason why they may decide not to
have this test.

For the test: _____

_____

Against the test: _____

_____ [2]

Total [5]

4 Use ideas about genes and alleles, and body cells and sex cells, to explain why member of a family of two parents and their two children show variation.

✎ The quality of written communication will be assessed in your answer to this question.

Write your answer on separate paper or in your exercise book.

Total [6]

5 Niemann-Pick disease is an inherited disorder. It is caused by a faulty allele. The faulty gene causes reduced appetite, unsteady walking, and slurring of speech.

Look at the family tree.

a Explain how the family tree shows that the faulty allele is recessive. **[2]**

b Name the people who are definitely carriers of the disease. **[1]**

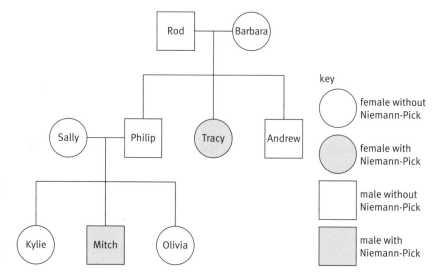

key

○ female without Niemann-Pick

⬤ female with Niemann-Pick

☐ male without Niemann-Pick

▨ male with Niemann-Pick

Going for the highest grades

c Name the people who must be homozygous for Niemann-Pick disease. **[1]**

d Use the example of Niemann-Pick disorder to help you explain the difference between the words *phenotype* and *genotype*. **[2]**

e Niemann-Pick is a serious disorder. It can cause death in childhood.

Sally and Matt want a baby. They are carriers of Niemann-Pick disorder. Their doctor suggests using their sperm and eggs to create embryos outside the body, and then performing pre-implantation genetic diagnosis on the embryos.

i Explain the meaning of the term *pre-implantation genetic diagnosis*. **[2]**

ii Describe some implications of pre-implantation genetic diagnosis. **[3]**

Write your answer on a separate piece of paper or in your exercise book.

Total [11]

Exam tip

Practise interpreting family tree diagrams.

1 Label the pie chart with the names of the gases of the Earth's atmosphere.

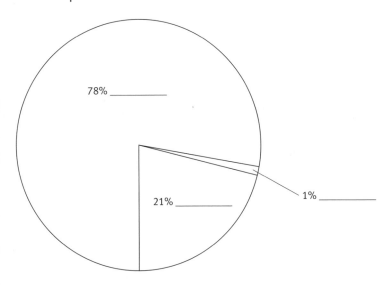

78% _____

21% _____

1% _____

2 Complete the captions to show how the Earth's atmosphere may have been formed.

The early atmosphere was mainly _____ and _____.

Water vapour _____ to form oceans. Carbon dioxide _____ in the oceans. Later it formed _____ rocks.

Early plants removed _____ from the atmosphere by photosynthesis, and added _____ to the atmosphere.

3 Write these formulas in sensible places on the drawings.

O_2 NO_2 CO_2 N_2 H_2O NO C CO

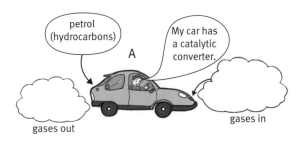

petrol (hydrocarbons)

My car has a catalytic converter.

A

gases out

gases in

petrol (hydrocarbons)

B

Cats didn't exist when they made this old banger!

gases out

gases in

4 Fill in the gaps.

Octane is a hydrocarbon. It is a compound that contains _____ and _____

only. When it burns, it reacts with _____ from the air to make _____

_____ and _____. This is a _____ reaction. There

are the same total _____ of atoms of each element in the reactants and in the

_____. The atoms are joined together differently after the reaction; they have

been _____. The properties of the _____ are different from the

properties of the reactants.

(H) The total mass of reactants is the same as the total mass of _____.

5 Fill in the empty boxes to summarise some combustion reactions of coal.

	Reactants		Product
Name	coal (with no sulfur impurities)	oxygen (from a plentiful supply of air)	
Formula	C	O_2	CO_2
Diagram			

	Reactants		Products		
Name	coal (with no sulfur impurities)	oxygen (from a limited supply of air)		carbon monoxide	particulate carbon
Formula	C		CO_2		C
Diagram					

	Reactants		Products		
Name	coal (with sulfur impurities)	oxygen (from a plentiful supply of air)			
Formula	C and S		CO_2	SO_2	
Diagram					

6 Write in the speech bubbles to finish what the people are saying.

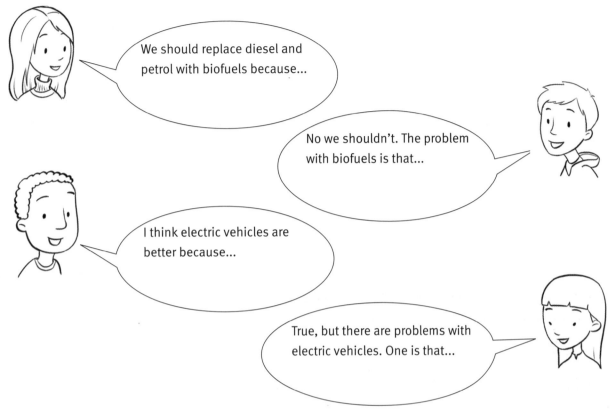

We should replace diesel and petrol with biofuels because...

No we shouldn't. The problem with biofuels is that...

I think electric vehicles are better because...

True, but there are problems with electric vehicles. One is that...

C 1

7 Fill in the empty boxes.

Pollutant name	Pollutant formula	Where the pollutant comes from	Problems the pollutant causes	One way of reducing the amount of this pollutant added to the atmosphere
sulfur dioxide				
nitrogen oxides				
carbon dioxide				
carbon monoxide				
particulate carbon				

C1.1.1–4 What is in the atmosphere?

The **atmosphere**, or air, is the layer of gases surrounding the Earth. It is a mixture of gases, each made up of small **molecules**. A molecule is a group of atoms joined together. In air, there are big spaces between the molecules. Clean air consists of:

*   78% nitrogen
*   21% oxygen
*   1% argon
*   small amounts of other gases, like water vapour and carbon dioxide.

Human activity and volcanic eruptions add other gases and **particulates** to the air. Particulates are tiny pieces of solid. Many of these gases and particulates are **pollutants**. They affect air quality.

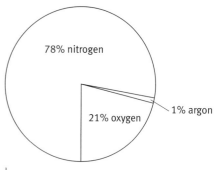

This pie chart shows the percentages of the main gases in clean air.

C1.1.5–8 How was the atmosphere formed?

The Earth's early atmosphere was probably mainly carbon dioxide and water vapour. These gases came from volcanoes.

The Earth cooled. Water vapour condensed to make oceans. Some carbon dioxide dissolved in the oceans, later making sedimentary rocks. Some of the carbon from the carbon dioxide ended up in fossil fuels.

Over time, the amount of oxygen in the air increased. This may have been the result of photosynthesis in early plants. The plants took carbon dioxide from the atmosphere, and added oxygen to the atmosphere.

C1.2.1–3, C1.2.7–9 How do reactions make air pollutants?

Coal is mainly **carbon**. Petrol, diesel, and fuel oil are mainly **hydrocarbons**. Hydrocarbons are compounds of hydrogen and carbon only. These **fossil fuels** burn in vehicles like cars and trains, and in power stations to generate electricity.

When fossil fuels burn they react with oxygen from the air. The main products are carbon dioxide and water (hydrogen oxide). Burning reactions are also called **combustion** reactions.

In all chemical reactions, the atoms are rearranged. The same atoms make up both the reactants and the products; they are just joined together differently.

This means that, in a chemical reaction, the total mass of products is equal to the total mass of reactants. Mass is conserved.

In all chemical reactions, the properties of the reactants and products are different.

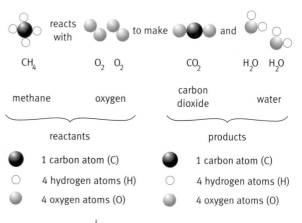

Methane (natural gas) reacts with oxygen to make carbon dioxide and water.

C1.2.4–6 What are oxidation and reduction reactions?

Oxidation reactions add oxygen to a chemical. The burning reactions of fuels are examples of oxidation reactions.

Fuels burn more quickly in pure oxygen than in air. Oxygen can be separated from the air. The oxygen can be used to support combustion reactions in oxy-fuel welding torches.

C1.9.1, C1.2.11–14 Where do air pollutants come from?

Burning fossil fuels make carbon dioxide. Sometimes there is not enough oxygen to convert all the carbon in the fuel to carbon dioxide. Then **incomplete burning** occurs. This makes carbon monoxide gas and particulate carbon.

Some fossil fuels contain sulfur. When the fuel burns, the sulfur reacts with oxygen to make sulfur dioxide.

At high temperatures inside vehicle engines, nitrogen and oxygen from the air react to make nitrogen oxides.

Name of pollutant	Formula	Diagram of molecule
carbon dioxide	CO_2	
carbon monoxide	CO	
sulfur dioxide	SO_2	
nitrogen monoxide	NO	
nitrogen dioxide	NO_2	
water	H_2O	

Nitrogen monoxide (NO) forms first. This reacts with more oxygen from the air to make nitrogen dioxide (NO_2). Together, NO and NO_2 are called NO_x.

The table shows the formulae of some products of burning reactions.

C1.1.10, C1.2.15 What problems do air pollutants cause?

Atmospheric pollutants do not just disappear. Some carbon dioxide from burning fossil fuels is used for photosynthesis. Some dissolves in rainwater and in the sea. The rest of the carbon dioxide remains in the atmosphere.

Some pollutants harm humans directly, including carbon monoxide. This reduces the amount of oxygen your blood can carry.

Some pollutants harm the environment. They may harm humans indirectly, including:

- Sulfur dioxide and oxides of nitrogen react with water and oxygen to make acid rain.
- Carbon dioxide contributes to climate change.
- Particulate carbon makes surfaces dirty.

Exam tip

Practise using the formulae in the table to draw the molecule diagrams.

C1.3.1–5 How can we improve air quality?

The only way of making less carbon dioxide is to burn smaller amounts of fossil fuels.

Power stations

We can reduce air pollution from fossil fuel power stations by:
- using less electricity
- removing sulfur impurities from natural gas and oil before burning
- removing sulfur dioxide and particulates from flue gases (the gases that power stations emit).

Ⓗ Sulfur dioxide is acidic. It is removed from flue gases by reacting it with an alkali in **wet scrubbing**. Two alkaline substances are used:
- Seawater – the flue gases are sprayed with seawater. Substances in the seawater react with sulfur dioxide.
- A slurry of calcium oxide powder and water – calcium oxide and sulfur dioxide react to make calcium sulfate. The calcium sulfate is used to make building plaster.

Vehicles

We can reduce air pollution from vehicle exhaust gases by:
- developing efficient engines that burn less fuel
- using low sulfur fuels
- using catalytic converters in vehicles to
  - add oxygen to carbon monoxide in an oxidation reaction. The product is carbon dioxide.
  - remove oxygen from nitrogen monoxide in a **reduction** reaction. The products are nitrogen and oxygen.
- using public transport instead of cars
- having legal limits on exhaust emissions, enforced by MOT tests
- fuelling vehicles with biofuels, or using electric vehicles.

Ⓗ **Biofuels** are made from plants like sugar cane. The plants take carbon dioxide from the atmosphere as they grow. When biofuels burn, carbon dioxide returns to the atmosphere. Biofuel plants grow on land that could be used for food crops.

Electric vehicles are powered by batteries. They do not produce waste gases during use. However, the electricity may have been generated by burning fossil fuels. Electric vehicles need recharging often.

Use extra paper to answer these questions if you need to.

1 Draw lines to link each pollutant to a problem it causes.

Pollutants
sulfur dioxide
carbon dioxide
carbon monoxide
particulate carbon

Problems
makes surfaces dirty
acid rain
reduces the amount of oxygen the blood carries
climate change

2 Complete the table to show the percentage of each gas in clean air.

Gas	Percentage in air
argon	
nitrogen	
oxygen	

3 Choose words from the box to fill in the gaps in the sentences below. The words in the box may be used once, more than once, or not at all.

> **carbon   nitrogen   oxygen   carbon dioxide**
>
> **hydrogen   carbon monoxide   hydrocarbons**

Coal contains mainly _____ . Petrol and diesel are mainly _____ . These are compounds made up of _____ and carbon only. When petrol burns, its atoms react with atoms from _____ molecules. The products of the reaction are mainly _____ and water.

4 Highlight the statements below that are **true**. Then write corrected versions of the statements that are **false**.
   a The air is a mixture of gases.
   b The spaces between molecules in the air are small.
   c Carbon monoxide is indirectly harmful to humans.
   d Nitrogen dioxide is indirectly harmful to humans.
   e Fuels burn more slowly in air than in pure oxygen.

5 The statements below describe some changes in the atmosphere. Write the letters of the steps in the order that they probably happened.
   A Burning fossil fuels added extra carbon dioxide to the atmosphere.
   B Water vapour condensed to form the oceans.
   C Volcanoes added carbon dioxide and water vapour to the atmosphere.
   D Early plants added oxygen to the atmosphere.

6 Explain how carbon dioxide gas was removed from the early atmosphere.

7 Highlight the one correct word or phrase in each pair of **bold** words.

Methane is a **hydrocarbon/particulate**. When it burns, it reacts with **nitrogen/oxygen** from the air in an **oxidation/reduction** reaction. In **oxidation/reduction** reactions, oxygen is lost from a substance.

8 Copy and complete the table.

Formula	Diagram of molecule	Name
CO		
		sulfur dioxide
		carbon dioxide
NO_2		
H_2O		
		nitrogen monoxide

9 List five ways of reducing the atmospheric pollution caused by exhaust emissions from motor vehicles.

10 The diagram below shows the molecules in the reaction of a hydrocarbon fuel, methane, with oxygen. Describe what the diagram tells you about the reaction.

H 11 Fill in the gaps in the sentences below.
At the high temperature of car engines, oxygen and _____ from the air react to make _____ _____ gas, with the formula _____ . This then reacts with more oxygen to make _____ _____ gas, with the formula _____ . Together, these oxides of nitrogen are referred to as _____ . Oxides of nitrogen cause _____ _____ .

12 Describe two ways of removing sulfur dioxide from power station flue gases by wet scrubbing.

13 List the benefits and problems of using biofuels to fuel cars.

14 Identify the advantages and disadvantages of electric cars, compared with diesel cars.

15 A scientist found that 3 g of a hydrocarbon used up 8 g of oxygen when it burned completely. Calculate the mass of carbon dioxide produced.

16 A scientist burned 12 g of carbon in pure oxygen. The reaction produced 44 g of carbon dioxide. Calculate the mass of oxygen that reacted with the carbon.

17 1 g of sulfur reacts with 1 g of oxygen. What mass of sulfur dioxide is made?

18 A scientist burned 4 g of methane in 16 g of oxygen. She made 11 g of carbon dioxide, and some water vapour. Calculate the mass of water vapour.

1 Menna does an experiment to estimate the percentage of oxygen in the air.

She heats some copper strongly whilst passing air over it, backwards and forwards, from two syringes.

The oxygen in the air in the syringes reacts with the copper.

Menna works out the decrease in the volume of air.

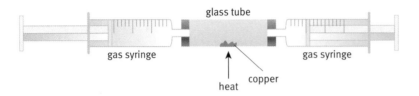

	Run 1	Run 2	Run 3	Run 4
Volume of air in syringes at start (cm³)	100	100	100	100
Volume of air in syringes at end (cm³)	82	86		84
Decrease in volume (cm³)	18		15	16

a Calculate the missing volumes.
  Write your answers in the table. [2]

b Select data from the table to calculate the mean decrease in volume.

  Mean volume = _____ cm³ [2]

c The expected decrease in volume is 21 cm³. Explain why.

  _____ [1]

d Suggest an explanation for the difference between the expected decrease in volume and the decrease in volume you calculated in part (b).

  _____

  _____ [1]

Total [6]

2 a i Sulfur dioxide is made when sulfur reacts with oxygen from the air.
Finish the diagram to represent this reaction.

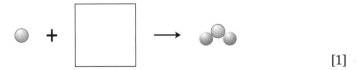

[1]

ii One source of sulfur is in the coal that power stations burn to generate electricity.
Name one other source of the sulfur that reacts to make sulfur dioxide.

_____ [1]

b The graph shows how the amount of sulfur dioxide emitted by China changed in the 1980s.

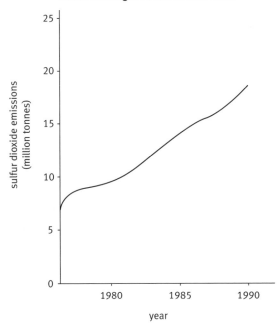

Sulfur dioxide gas emissions from China

i Use the graph to complete the sentence below.

Between 1980 and 1990 the amount of sulfur dioxide emitted by China _____.[1]

ii Suggest why the amount of sulfur dioxide emitted by China changed in this way.

_____ [1]

c **i** Sulfur dioxide mixes with other gases in the atmosphere.

Circle the names of the two gases in the Earth's atmosphere that are present in the two largest amounts.

nitrogen   carbon dioxide   oxygen   argon hydrogen [2]

ii In the atmosphere, sulfur dioxide reacts with water to make acid rain.

Why is acid rain a problem?

Put ticks in the three correct boxes.

Acid rain damages buildings made of limestone. ☐

Acid rain makes lakes more acidic. ☐

Acid rain damages trees. ☐

Acid rain increases the pH of streams. ☐ [2]

d This graph shows how the amount of sulfur dioxide emitted by the UK has changed since 1980.

Describe the trend shown by the graph. [1]

Total [9]

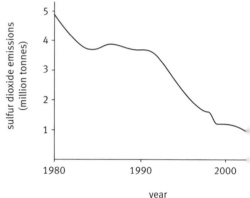

Sulfur dioxide gas emissions from the UK

Going for the highest grades

3 Cars burn hydrocarbon fuels. Carbon dioxide is a product of these burning reactions. The table shows the masses and carbon dioxide emissions of some Volkswagen cars.

Car model	Minimum car mass (kg)	Average CO_2 emissions in g / km
Fox	978	144
Polo	1000	138
New Golf	1142	149
Touran	1423	176
Toureg	2214	324

A student says that the data shows that heavier cars cause increased carbon dioxide emissions.

Do you think the student is correct? Use data from the table, as well as your own knowledge and understanding, to support your decision.

✎ The quality of written communication will be assessed in your answer to this question.

Write your answer on separate paper or in your exercise book.

Total [6]

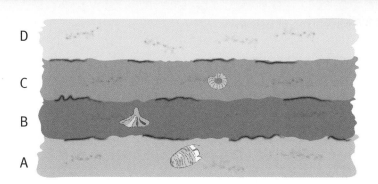

This diagram shows sedimentary rock containing fossils. Assume that this rock has never been folded.

1 Give the letter of

a the layer that contains the youngest fossils _____

b the layer made of the oldest rocks _____

c the layer made of the youngest rocks _____

d the layer in which sediments were first deposited _____

2 Write the correct numbers in the gaps. Use the numbers in the box.

> **12 700   10   14 thousand million**
>
> **five thousand million   four thousand million**

a The diameter of the Earth is about _____ km.

b The Earth's oldest rocks are _____ years old.

c Seafloors spread by about _____ cm each year.

d The Sun was formed about _____ years ago.

e The 'big bang' happened about _____ years ago.

3 Write the letters of the distances below in order, smallest first. The first one has been done for you.

| G | | | | | | | | |

A the diameter of the Sun

B the diameter of the Milky Way

C the distance from the Milky Way to the nearest galaxy

D the distance from the Sun to the nearest star

E the diameter of the Earth

F the diameter of Earth's Moon

G the diameter of a comet

H the diameter of the Earth's orbit

I the diameter of the Solar System

Exam tip

Remember this order of distances. You may be asked about it in the exam.

P 1

4 List one or more differences between the objects in each pair below.

a comet and asteroid _____

_____

b moon and planet _____

_____

c star and galaxy _____

_____

5 Draw lines to match each type of wave to:
- the direction of vibrations
- one or more examples.

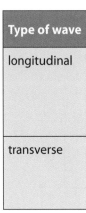

Direction of vibrations	Type of wave
vibrations are at right angles to the direction in which the wave is moving	longitudinal
vibrations are in the same direction as the moving wave	transverse

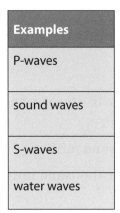

Examples
P-waves
sound waves
S-waves
water waves

6 Draw and label two arrows on the diagram to show the wave's **wavelength** and **amplitude**.

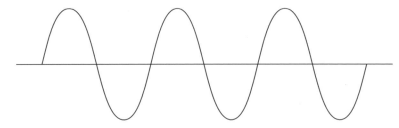

7 Calculate the speed of these waves. Include units in your answers.

a a sound wave from a firework that travels 100 m in 0.3 seconds

Answer = _____

b a seismic wave that has a wavelength of 20 km and a frequency of 0.5 Hz

Answer = _____

Exam tip

There are two equations that include wave speed. Make sure you choose the right one!

P1.1.1–3 What is the Solar System?

Our **Solar System** was formed about 5000 million years ago from clouds of gases and dust in space. It contains:

- the **Sun**, the star at the centre of the Solar System
- eight **planets**, including **Earth**
- **dwarf planets**, including Pluto
- **moons** – natural satellites that orbit some planets
- **comets** – big lumps of ice and dust
- **asteroids** – lumps of rock that are smaller than planets.

Type of body	Diameter (km)	Orbit
Planet	Mercury, 4880 (smallest) Saturn, 120 000 (biggest) Earth, 12 700	almost circular path around the Sun
Dwarf planet	Pluto, 2306	elliptical path around the Sun
Moon	Earth's moon, 3500 A moon is smaller than the planet it orbits.	circular path around a planet
Comets	a few kilometres	rush past the Sun then return to the outer Solar System
Asteroids	up to 1000; most are much smaller	almost circular, mostly between Mars and Jupiter

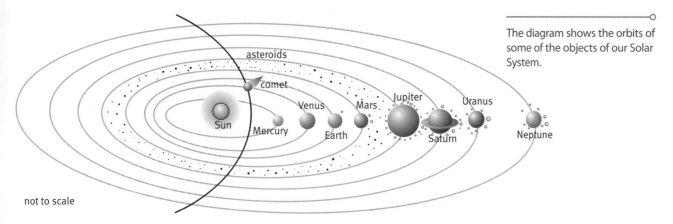

not to scale

The diagram shows the orbits of some of the objects of our Solar System.

P1.1.4–5, P1.1.15–16 What is the Universe?

The Sun is a star. It is a ball of hot gases, mainly hydrogen. In the Sun, hydrogen atom nuclei join together by **nuclear fusion**. This releases energy and creates helium. All the other elements were made by fusion reactions in stars.

There are thousands of millions of stars in our **galaxy**, the Milky Way. The **Universe** is made up of thousands of millions of galaxies.

P1.1.7–14 How do we find out about stars?

Astronomers can learn about other stars and galaxies only by studying the radiation they emit. They measure the distance to stars from their **relative brightness**, or by **parallax**.

There are **uncertainties** about distances in space. This is because making accurate observations is difficult. Also, astronomers make **assumptions** when interpreting observations.

Light travels through space (a vacuum) at 300 000 km/s. So when astronomers observe a distant object they see what it looked like when light left the object – not what it looks like now. Astronomers measure distances in light-years. One light-year is the distance light travels through a vacuum in one year.

Light pollution near cities makes it difficult to observe stars. So astronomers set up telescopes away from big cities.

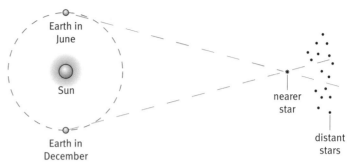

The Earth moves from one side of the Sun to the other. Nearby stars seem to move compared with the background of distant stars. The nearer a star is to Earth, the more it seems to move. This is **parallax**.

P1.1.17–22 How is the Universe changing?

Other galaxies are moving away from us. This is evidence that the Universe started with a 'big bang', about 14 000 million years ago.

(H) Evidence that galaxies are moving apart comes from **redshift.** This means that light from galaxies is shifted towards the red end of the spectrum. Galaxies that are further away from us move faster than those that are closer. This is evidence that space is expanding.

It is difficult to predict how the Universe will end. This is because it is difficult to study the motion of distant objects, and to measure huge distances.

(H) It is difficult to work out the mass of the Universe.

P1.2.1–4 What can we learn from rocks?

Evidence from rocks tells us about the structure of the Earth. For example, the Earth must be older than its oldest rocks, which are about 4000 million years old. Geologists use **radioactive dating** to estimate rocks' ages.

Rock processes we see today explain past changes. For example, mountains are being made all the time – if not, **erosion** would wear down continents to sea level. **Sedimentation** explains why older rocks are usually found under younger rocks.

Older rocks are usually found under younger rocks. Different creatures lived at different times in the past. Their fossils can help geologists decide when rocks were formed.

P1.2.5–7 What is Wegener's theory?

In 1912, Wegener suggested his theory of **continental drift**. He explained that today's continents were once joined together. For millions of years, they have been slowly moving apart. This explains why there are mountain chains at the edges of continents.

For more details about Wegener's theory, see page 132.

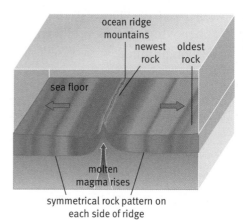

The Earth as it was 250 million years ago.

P1.2.8–10 What is seafloor spreading?

Scientists detected **ocean ridges**, which are lines of mountains under the sea. New ocean floor is made at these ridges. So seafloors spread by about 10 cm a year.

New ocean floor is made when material from the solid mantle rise slowly. Some of the mantle material melts to form magma. Movements in the mantle, caused by convection, pull an ocean ridge apart. Magma erupts and cools to make new rock.

The new rock has a symmetrical pattern of magnetic stripes. This is because as magma solidifies, it becomes magnetised in the direction of the Earth's magnetic field at the time.

Seafloor spreading makes new rock.

P1.2.11–12 What is plate tectonics?

The outer layer of the Earth is made of about 12 huge pieces of rock, called **tectonic plates**. They move slowly all the time. Earthquakes, volcanoes, and mountain building usually happen where tectonic plates meet.

- In the Himalayas, plates move towards each other. They collide. The edges of the continents crumple together and pile up. This **builds mountains**.
- Most **volcanoes** are at plate boundaries where the crust is stretching or being compressed.
- In some places, tectonic plates slide past each other. Huge forces build up along fault lines. The forces become so big that the locked-together rocks break, and the plates move. The ground shakes. This is an **earthquake**.
- The movement of tectonic plates contributes to the rock cycle.

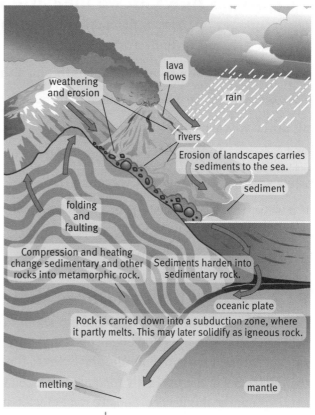

The movement of tectonic plates also plays a part in the rock cycle.

P1.2.13–14 What are seismic waves?

Earthquakes release energy. The energy spreads out as vibrations, or **seismic waves**. Seismometers detect waves on the Earth's surface. Two types of waves produced by earthquakes are:
- P-waves, which travel through solids and liquids
- S-waves, which travel through solids but not liquids.

P1.2.15, P1.2.19 What are waves?

A **wave** is a travelling vibration that transfers energy from place to place without transferring matter. There are two types of wave:

- **Longitudinal waves** travel as compressions. The particles vibrate in the same direction as the moving wave. Sound waves and P-waves are longitudinal.

- In a **transverse wave**, the particles vibrate at 90° to the direction of the wave's movement. Water waves and S-waves are transverse.

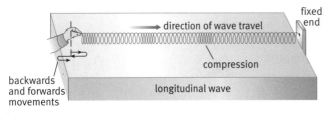

A longitudinal wave is made by compressing and releasing the spring.

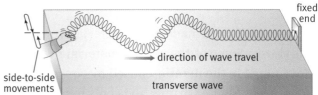

A transverse wave is made by moving the spring from side to side.

P1.2.20–23 How can we measure waves?

The **frequency** of a wave is the number of waves that pass any point each second. Its units are hertz (Hz).

The diagram shows a wave's **wavelength** and **amplitude**.

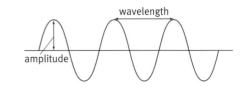

The distance a wave travels is linked to its speed:

distance = wave speed × time

This equation links speed to frequency and wavelength:

wave speed = frequency × wavelength

If a wave travels at a constant speed, its frequency is inversely proportional to its wavelength:

$$\text{frequency} \propto \frac{1}{\text{wavelength}}$$

P1.2.16–17 What can waves show us?

Geologists used seismic waves to find out about the Earth's structure. P-waves travel through solids and liquids, so they can get through the core, mantle, and crust to the other side of the Earth. S-waves travel only through solids. So they cannot get through the liquid core, and are not detected in the S-wave **shadow zone**.

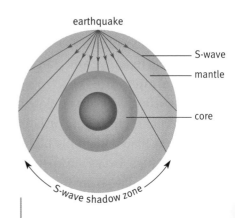

S-waves from an earthquake are blocked from reaching almost half of the Earth's surface.

Use extra paper to answer these questions if you need to.

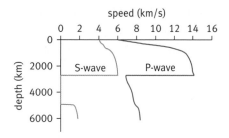

1 Add labels to the diagram of the Earth to show the crust, mantle, and core.

2 Tick the boxes to show which objects below emit light.
   a the planet Jupiter
   b the Sun
   c the star Sirius
   d the Moon
   e comets

3 Choose words from the box to fill in the gaps. The words may be used once, more than once, or not at all.

uncertainties	assumptions
brightness	parallax	pollution

The distance to a star can be estimated from its relative _____ . It is difficult to make accurate observations of the night sky in cities because of light _____ . Even without this problem, there are _____ about the distances to stars. This is partly because scientists need to make _____ when interpreting observations.

4 Write definitions for the words below:
   a wave
   b frequency
   c wavelength
   d amplitude
   e light-year.

5 Calculate the distance travelled by each of the following waves:
   a An S-wave that travels at an average speed of 5 km/s for 410 seconds.
   b A P-wave that travels at an average speed of 10 km/s for 205 seconds.
   c A sound wave that travels at a speed of 340 m/s for 60 seconds.

6 The statements below describe how new rock is formed on the seafloor. Write the letters of the steps in the best order.
   A Some mantle material melts.
   B Magma erupts at the middle of the ridge.
   C Material from the solid mantle rises slowly.

D This forms magma.

E It cools to make new rock.

7 List three pieces of evidence Wegener used to support his theory of continental drift.

8 List three reasons to explain why Wegener's theory was not at first accepted by geologists.

9 Calculate the speed of each of the waves below.
   a a wave from an earthquake with a frequency of 0.5 Hz and a wavelength of 15 km
   b a wave from an earthquake with a frequency of 0.5 Hz and a wavelength of 18 km

10 The graph shows how the speeds of an S-wave and a P-wave change at they travel through the Earth.

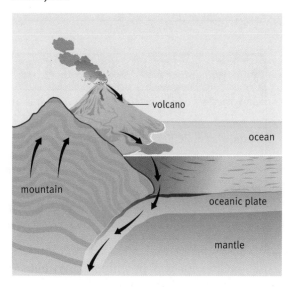

   a Use the graph to estimate the depth at which the Earth's solid mantle meets the liquid outer core.
   b Describe the evidence on the graph that supports the theory that Earth has a liquid outer core.

H 11 Describe evidence for the explanations below:
   a Distant galaxies are moving away from us.
   b Space itself is expanding.
   c The Earth's magnetic field can change direction.

12 Annotate the diagram below to show how the movement of tectonic plates contributes to the rock cycle.

P 1

1 Read the article.

a Read the following statements.

Put a tick (√) in the box next to each of the three correct statements.

Galileo saw Ganymede through a telescope. ☐

Ganymede is a star. ☐

Gan Dej saw an object close to Jupiter without a telescope. ☐

Ganymede is a moon. ☐

Gan Dej definitely saw Ganymede. ☐

Galileo was definitely the first person to see Ganymede. ☐ [3]

b Use the information below, and the data in the table, to evaluate whether or not it might have been possible for Gan Dej to have seen Ganymede 2000 years before Galileo, without a telescope.

The *apparent magnitude* of an object in Space is a measure of its brightness as seen from Earth. The table gives some values for apparent magnitude. The smaller the apparent magnitude, the brighter the object.

Apparent magnitude	Object
between 3 and 4	Faintest object in Space that can be seen from a modern city without a telescope .
4.4	Ganymede
6.5	Faintest object in Space that can be seen in a very dark sky without a telescope

_____

_____ [2]

c

Name of object	Approximate diameter (km)	Object it orbits	Other information
Ganymede	5362	Jupiter	It is one of many objects that orbits Jupiter.
Xena	3000	Sun	Made from gases and dust when the Solar System began.
Pluto	2400	Sun	Its mass is less than the total mass of the other objects that cross its orbit.

i Give one way in which Ganymede **does not** fit the definition of a planet.

_____ [1]

Who first saw Ganymede?
Many astronomers accept that Galileo was the first person to see Jupiter's moon Ganymede. Galileo used a telescope to make his observations in 1610.

However, there is evidence that a Chinese astronomer, Gan Dej, first saw Ganymede about 2000 years earlier. Gan Dej reported a 'small reddish star' next to Jupiter. This could have been the moon we now call Ganymede. However, Gan Dej did not have a telescope. The moons of Jupiter are not bright enough for their colours to be seen without a telescope.

In August 2006, the International Astronomical Union defined a planet as a body that orbits a star, and has a spherical shape. The mass of a planet must be much greater than the total mass of the other objects that cross its orbit.

ii Give one way in which Pluto **does not** fit the definition of a planet.

_____ [1]

iii Give one way in which Xena **does** fit the definition of a planet.

_____ [1]

Total [8]

2 a On the diagram of the Earth, label the **crust**, **mantle**, and **core**. [2]

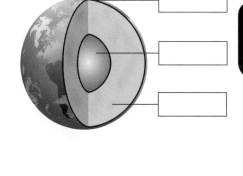

b Draw straight lines to match each **explanation** with **evidence** that supports it.

Explanation	Evidence
1 South America and Africa were once part of one big continent.	**A** Scientists have found many craters.
2 Mountains are being formed all the time.	**B** Radioactive dating of rocks.
3 The Earth is older than 4000 million years.	**C** Scientists have found the same fossils on both sides of the Atlantic Ocean.
4 Asteroids have collided with Earth.	**D** Rocks are continually eroded but the continents are not all at sea level.

[3]

Total [5]

3 A seismometer detects seismic waves from earthquakes. It records data on seismographs like the one below.

a Use the graph on the right to decide which travel faster: S-waves or P-waves. Explain your decision.

_____

_____ [1]

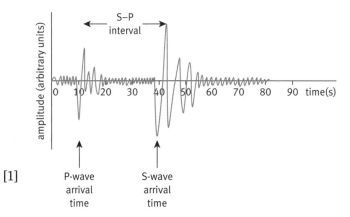

b

On a seismograph, scientists use the S-P interval to calculate the distance from the centre of the earthquake to the seismometer. The S-P interval is marked on the seismograph on the previous page. The shorter the S-P interval, the closer the seismometer was to the earthquake.

The seismographs on the right are from the same earthquake.

They were obtained from seismometers in different parts of the world.

i Give the S-P interval shown on each seismograph. Write your answers in the table below.

seismograph	S-P time interval (s)
A	
B	
C	

[1]

(A) Seismograph

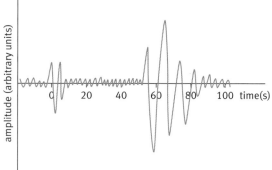

(B) Seismograph

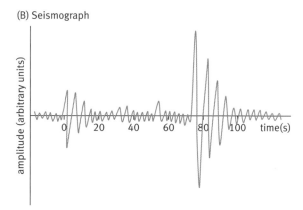

(C) Seismograph

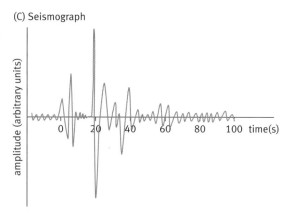

ii Use your answer to part (i) and the information in the box to state which seismograph was recorded closest to the earthquake. Explain your decision.

_____

_____ [1]

c i Assume the S waves from the earthquake travelled at a speed of 5 km/s. Calculate the distance they travelled in 60 seconds. Show your working.

Answer = _____ km [2]

ii The table shows the distance of three towns from the centre of the earthquake.

Town	distance from centre of earthquake (km)
Owlton	250
Foxford	670
Badgerbridge	290

Which town or towns would S-waves from the earthquake have reached in 60 seconds or less?

_____ [1]

Total [6]

Exam tip

Make sure you know the differences between S-waves and P-waves.

1 Write each phrase from the box in a sensible place on the flow diagram.

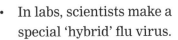

> **damage cells**
>
> **disease symptoms**
>
> **reproduce rapidly**
>
> **make toxins**

Harmful microorganisms enter the body.

or

B 2

2 Here are the stages in making an influenza (flu) vaccine.

- Experts meet every April to decide which strain of wild flu virus is likely to attack next winter.
- In labs, scientists make a special 'hybrid' flu virus.
- This flu virus is delivered around the world.
- Technicians drill holes in fertilised hens' eggs.
- Technicians inject the flu virus into the eggs and seal the hole with wax.
- The eggs provide food and moisture. They are kept warm at about 37 °C for 10 days.
- Technicians harvest the flu virus from the eggs.
- Technicians break the flu virus into pieces and put it into the vaccine.

  a Underline the stage that takes account of the fact that the flu virus changes very quickly.

  b Draw a box around the stage that shows the conditions the flu virus needs to reproduce quickly.

  c Draw a cloud around the stage that shows how the virus is made safe before being put into the vaccine.

  d Draw a triangle around the stage that indicates that the flu virus spreads easily from person to person.

H **3** Look at captions **A** to **L** below. Write one letter in each box to show how water balance is controlled in the body. Two have been done for you.

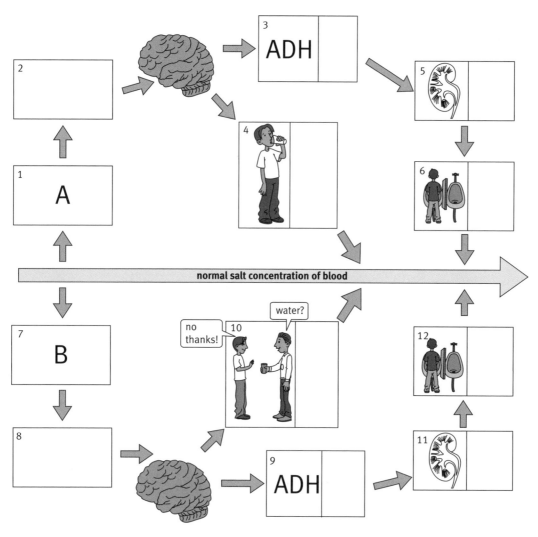

A The concentration of the blood plasma increases.

B The concentration of the blood plasma decreases.

C Receptors in the brain are stimulated.

D ADH is secreted by the pituitary gland.

E More water is reabsorbed in the kidneys.

F Less urine is made. It is concentrated.

G Receptors in the brain are not stimulated.

H Less ADH is secreted by the pituitary gland.

I Less water is reabsorbed by the kidneys.

J More urine is made. It is dilute.

K The person feels thirsty and drinks water.

L The person does not feel thirsty, so drinks little water.

B2.1.1–6 How do our bodies resist infection?

Inside your body, conditions are ideal for **microorganisms** like bacteria and viruses. So they reproduce quickly. Some bacteria and viruses cause infectious diseases. They give you disease symptoms by damaging cells or making poisons (**toxins**).

White blood cells try to destroy harmful microorganisms. They are part of your **immune system**. One type of white blood cell **engulfs** and **digests** harmful microorganisms. Another type of white blood cell makes **antibodies**.

Some of the white blood cells that make each antibody stay in your blood. These are **memory cells**. If the same microorganism invades your body in future, memory cells recognise its antigens. The memory cells quickly make the correct antibodies. The invaders are destroyed before you feel ill. You are **immune** to the disease.

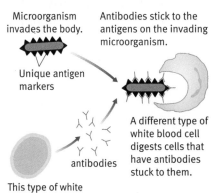

Microorganism invades the body.

Unique antigen markers

Antibodies stick to the antigens on the invading microorganism.

This type of white blood cell makes antibodies.

antibodies

A different type of white blood cell digests cells that have antibodies stuck to them.

One type of white blood cell makes antibodies to label microorganisms. A different type digests the microorganisms.

B2.2.1–5 How do vaccines work?

Vaccines prevent you getting diseases. A vaccine contains a safe form of a disease-causing microorganism. When a vaccine is injected into your body, white blood cells make antibodies against the microorganism. Your body stores some of these memory cells. If an active form of the microorganism enters your blood in future, memory cells quickly make antibodies. You do not get ill.

Having vaccinations is not risk free. Different people have different side-effects from vaccinations because they have different genes.

To prevent epidemics of infectious diseases, a high percentage of the population must be vaccinated. If they are not, large numbers of the disease-causing microorganism will remain in infected people, and people who cannot be vaccinated are likely to catch the disease.

B2.2.6–10 How do antibiotics work?

Antimicrobials are chemicals that may kill bacteria, fungi, and viruses.

Some types of antimicrobial **inhibit** the reproduction of microorganisms.

Antibiotics are effective against bacteria, but not viruses.

Over time, some bacteria and fungi become **resistant** to antimicrobials. To reduce antibiotic resistance, people must:
*   finish all the tablets, even if they feel better
*   only use antibiotics when necessary.

B 2

Ⓗ Antimicrobial resistance develops when random changes (mutations) in the genes of bacteria or fungi make new varieties that the antimicrobial cannot kill or inhibit.

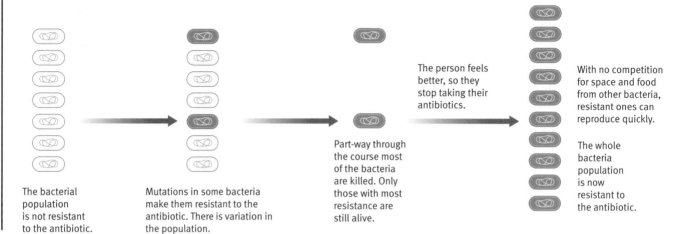

The bacterial population is not resistant to the antibiotic.

Mutations in some bacteria make them resistant to the antibiotic. There is variation in the population.

The person feels better, so they stop taking their antibiotics.

Part-way through the course most of the bacteria are killed. Only those with most resistance are still alive.

With no competition for space and food from other bacteria, resistant ones can reproduce quickly.

The whole bacteria population is now resistant to the antibiotic.

A few mutations can result in antibiotic-resistant bacteria.

B2.2.11–15 How are new drugs trialled?

In most human trials on ill people, one group of patients takes the new drug. Another group of patients are **controls**. The controls take either the existing treatment for the illness, or a placebo.

A **placebo** looks like the new treatment, but has no drugs in it. Placebos are rarely used in human trials because people who take them miss out on the benefits of both new and existing treatments.

Ⓗ There are three types of human trial:
- In **double-blind** trials, neither patients nor doctors know who is in which group.
- In **blind** trials, doctors know who is in which group, but patients do not.
- In an **open-label** trial both the patient and their doctor knows whether the patient is given the new drug. These trials are used when the patient cannot affect the outcome of using the drug.

Long-term human trials ensure that the drug is safe and that it works. They also identify side-effects that do not occur immediately.

A new drug is tested for safety and effectiveness on lab-grown human cells and animals.

healthy volunteers to test for safety

people with the illness to test for effectiveness and safety

human trials

B2.3.1–7 How does your heart work?

Your heart pumps blood around your body. It is a **double pump**:
- The right lower chamber pumps blood to your lungs.
- The left lower chamber pumps blood to the rest of your body.

Your heart is made from muscle. It has its own blood supply. The blood brings oxygen and glucose to the heart. Heart cells use these as a supply of energy.

Blood travels around your body through **arteries**, **veins**, and **capillaries**. Blood vessels are well adapted to their functions:

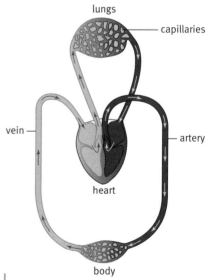

lungs

capillaries

vein

artery

heart

body

Blood flow around the body.

- **Arteries** take blood from the heart to your body. Their walls withstand the high pressure created by the pumping heart.

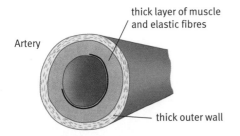

Artery
thick layer of muscle and elastic fibres
thick outer wall

- **Veins** have thin walls that can be squashed when you move. This pushes blood back to the heart.

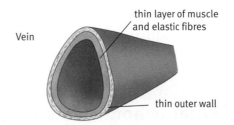

Vein
thin layer of muscle and elastic fibres
thin outer wall

- **Capillaries** take blood to and from tissues. Their very thin walls allow oxygen and food to diffuse into cells and waste to diffuse out of cells.

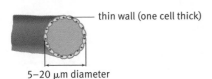

thin wall (one cell thick)

5–20 μm diameter

Exam tip

Revise the differences between arteries, veins, and capillaries carefully.

B 2

Doctors can check how well your heart is working. They measure:
- **pulse rate** at your wrist (the number of beats per minute)
- **blood pressure** – this measures the pressure of the blood on the walls of your arteries. It has two numbers. The higher number is the pressure when the heart is contracting. The lower number is the pressure when the heart is relaxing. Height, weight, gender, and lifestyle affect blood pressure, so there is a range of 'normal' blood pressure.

B2.3.8–16 What causes heart attacks?

Coronary arteries carry oxygenated blood to the heart. Fat can build up on the artery walls. A blood clot may form on this fat. This may block the artery. The blockage stops oxygen getting to the heart muscle. Heart cells die, and the heart is permanently damaged. This is a **heart attack**.

Your genes and your **lifestyle** affect your chances of having a heart attack. Poor diet, stress, and high blood pressure increase the risk of heart disease. So does misusing drugs such as nicotine (in cigarettes), alcohol, cannabis, and Ecstasy. Regular exercise reduces the risk of heart disease.

Heart disease is more common in the UK than in less industrialised countries. This may be because British people eat less healthily, or have higher levels of stress or drug misuse.

Scientists use **epidemiological studies** to identify risk factors for heart disease. These studies look at large numbers of people.

They often compare groups of people, for example, smokers and non-smokers. The two groups of people must be **matched**. This means they should be similar apart from the factor being tested.

In large-scale **genetic** studies, scientists compare the genes of people with a disease with those of healthy people. This helps identify alleles that increase the risk of a person getting the disease.

B2.4.1–5 What is homeostasis?

Automatic control systems keep body conditions constant. They are controlled by nervous and hormonal communication systems. Keeping a constant internal environment is called **homeostasis**.

Body control systems have:
- **receptors** to detect changes in the environment
- **processing centres** to receive information and coordinate responses automatically
- **effectors** to produce responses.

Your body's temperature and water control systems are automatic.

H They use **negative feedback** between the effector and the receptor of a control system to reverse changes to the system's steady state.

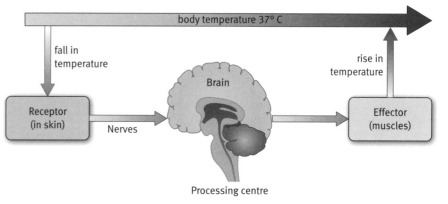

The diagram shows how body temperature is controlled automatically.

B2.4.6–13 How do we control water levels?

Cells only work properly if the concentrations of their contents are correct. So their water levels must be kept constant.

Your kidneys get rid of waste products by **excretion**. They also control water levels in your body. They do this by responding to water levels in **blood plasma**.

Water levels in your blood plasma may go down because of:
- sweating after exercise or on a hot day
- eating salty food
- not drinking much water.

When water levels in blood plasma are low, your kidneys make less urine. The urine is concentrated, so it is dark. When water levels in blood plasma are high, your kidneys make lots of dilute urine.

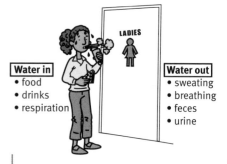

Your body loses and gains water to keep water levels balanced.

Kidneys are part of a negative feedback system.
- Receptors in the brain detect changes in concentration in blood plasma.
- If the concentration is too high, the **pituitary gland** in the brain releases **ADH** (a hormone) into the blood stream.
- The ADH travels to the kidneys (**effectors**). The more ADH that arrives, the more water the kidneys reabsorb into the body. So the more concentrated the urine.

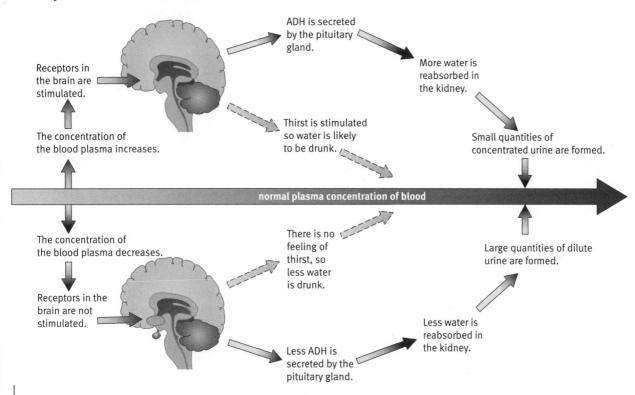

ADH is secreted by the pituitary gland.

Receptors in the brain are stimulated.

More water is reabsorbed in the kidney.

The concentration of the blood plasma increases.

Thirst is stimulated so water is likely to be drunk.

Small quantities of concentrated urine are formed.

normal plasma concentration of blood

The concentration of the blood plasma decreases.

There is no feeling of thirst, so less water is drunk.

Large quantities of dilute urine are formed.

Receptors in the brain are not stimulated.

Less water is reabsorbed in the kidney.

Less ADH is secreted by the pituitary gland.

Water balance is controlled by negative feedback, involving both nervous and hormonal communication.

Drugs affect the amount of urine you make:
- Alcohol leads to big volumes of dilute urine, so you may get dehydrated.
  This is because alcohol stops the pituitary gland releasing ADH.
- Taking Ecstasy leads to small volumes of concentrated urine.
  This is because Ecstasy makes the pituitary gland release more ADH.

Use extra paper to answer these questions if you need to.

1 Tick the boxes to show how to reduce the risk of heart disease.

   a Eat more fatty food. ☐
   b Do not smoke. ☐
   c Avoid stress. ☐
   d Do not exercise. ☐
   e Smoke cannabis occasionally. ☐
   f Keep your blood pressure high. ☐

2 Write an L next to the processes by which your body loses water, and a G next to the processes by which your body gains water.

   a eating food   c urinating   e producing feces
   b sweating   d breathing   f respiration

3 Draw lines to match each measurement with its definition.

Measurement	Definition
pulse rate	pressure against artery wall when heart is contracting
lower blood pressure measurement	number of heart beats per minute
higher blood pressure measurement	pressure against artery wall when heart is relaxed

4 Highlight the statements below that are **true**. Then write corrected versions of the statements that are **false**.

   a Antibiotics kill viruses.
   b Antimicrobials kill viruses, bacteria, and fungi.
   c New drugs are tested for effectiveness on human cells grown in the lab.
   d In clinical trials, new drugs are tested for effectiveness on healthy volunteers.
   e A placebo has no drugs in it.

5 Complete the table.

Part of circulation system	What does it do?	What is it made from?
heart	pumps blood around the body	
artery		
vein		thin walls made of muscle and elastic fibres
capillary		

6 The steps below describe how a vaccine works. Write the letters of the steps in the best order.

   A The vaccine is made from a safe form of the virus.
   B White blood cells digest the clump.
   C The vaccine is injected into the person.
   D Sometime later an active form of the virus gets into the blood.
   E Memory cells quickly make the correct antibodies.
   F White blood cells make antibodies that stick to the antigens on the safe form of the virus. Some of these white blood cells are stored in the body as memory cells.
   G The antibodies make the viruses clump together.

7 Draw lines to match each part of the control system to what it does.

Part of control system	What it does
receptor	receives information and processes responses
processing centre	detects changes in environment
effector	produces the response

8 Explain why taking vaccines and medicines is not risk free.

9 List two things people can do to help to reduce antibiotic resistance.

Ⓗ10 Write a P next to any trial types in which the patient knows whether or not she is in the control group. Write a D next to any trial types in which the doctor knows whether or not the patient is in the control group.

   a double-blind trial
   b blind trial
   c open-label trial

11 Explain the purpose of long-term human trials for new drugs.

12 MRSA is a type of bacteria that is resistant to most types of antibiotics. Explain how resistant bacteria develop.

13 The diagram shows the negative feedback system in a premature babies' incubator. Annotate the diagram to show how it is similar to the negative feedback system that controls water levels in the human body.

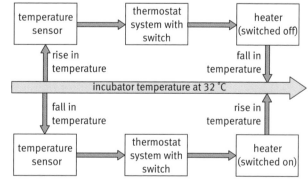

14 Explain the effects that alcohol and Ecstasy have on levels of ADH, and how this affects urine production.

1 Lauren has food poisoning. She has diarrhoea and vomits frequently.

She became ill after she ate a raw egg that contained *Salmonella* bacteria.

a The graph shows the changes in the number of *Salmonella* bacteria in Lauren's stomach.

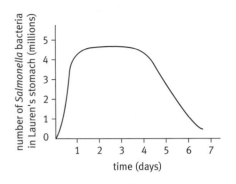

i Name the process that causes the number of bacteria to increase during the first few hours.

_____ [1]

ii Use the graph to complete the sentence below.

Lauren will probably begin to feel better _____ days after she ate the raw egg.

b Lauren's body tries to get rid of *Salmonella* bacteria in two ways:
- Vomiting and diarrhoea remove some of the bacteria from the intestines.
- Certain blood cells can destroy the bacteria.

i Name the type of blood cells that can destroy *Salmonella* bacteria.

_____ [1]

ii Suggest why Lauren's doctor advised her **not** to take anti-diarrhoea tablets.

_____

_____ [1]

Total [3]

B2

2 The graph shows the percentage of British 2-year-olds who received the MMR vaccine from 1989 to 2002. The MMR vaccine prevents people getting measles, mumps, and rubella.

a Here are some people's opinions about the triple MMR vaccine.

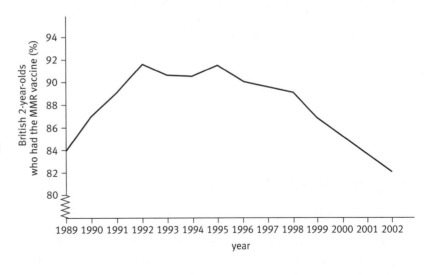

A I'm worried about the vaccine's possible serious side effects on my child.

B I'm a doctor. No vaccine is completely safe. The side effects of the MMR vaccine are a possible risk, but the dangers of measles, mumps, and rubella are worse.

C Measles is a nasty disease. I don't want to risk my child getting it.

D The more children who have the MMR vaccine, the better. Then everyone is protected from measles, mumps, and rubella.

Use the graph and the opinions **A, B, C, and D** to complete the sentences below.

Between 1989 and 1992 the percentage of children who had the MMR vaccine _____ .

One opinion that may explain this trend is opinion _____ . Between 1992 and 2001

the percentage of children who had the MMR vaccine _____ . One opinion that may

explain this trend is opinion _____ .   [2]

b   Matthew had the MMR vaccine when he was one year old. Two years later, the measles virus got into his body.

Matthew did not get measles. The stages below explain why.

A   A nurse injects Matthew with the MMR vaccine. The vaccine contains safe forms of measles, mumps, and rubella viruses.

B   These cells make antibodies very quickly.

C   The natural measles virus gets into Matthew's bloodstream.

D   The virus is destroyed before it has time to make Matthew feel ill.

E   Matthew's white blood cells make antibodies to recognise measles, mumps, and rubella viruses.

F   Memory cells recognise the virus.

G   The level of antibodies in Matthew's blood falls over the next two years.

The stages are in the wrong order. Write a letter in each empty box to show the correct order.

A					

[4]

Total [6]

Answer this question if you expect to take the Foundation tier test.

3 Explain why and how water levels in the cells of a human body are kept constant, and how alcohol and Ecstasy affect the amount and concentration of urine a person makes.

✎ The quality of written communication will be assessed in your answer to this question.

Write your answer on separate paper or in your exercise book.

Total [6]

Going for the highest grades

Answer this question if you expect to take the Higher tier test.

4 Explain how a negative feedback system keeps water levels constant in the cells of a human body. In your answer, include the names of the hormone and organs involved in the system.

✎ The quality of written communication will be assessed in your answer to this question.

Write your answer on separate paper or in your exercise book.

Total [6]

> **Exam tip**
>
> When answering 6-mark questions:
> • Make sure you know what the question is asking you to do.
> • Write down key words to help answer the question.
> • Organise the key words in a sensible order.
> • Write your answer.
> • Check your spelling, punctuation, and grammar.

1 Look at the drawing of a child's tricycle.
Fill in the table.

Part of tricycle	Properties this part of the tricycle must have	Material
tyres		
brake		
frame		
seat		
handle to push tricycle		
pushing pole		
screws that join pushing pole to handle		
bag		

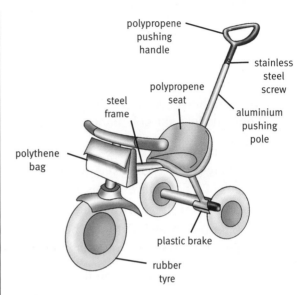

polypropene pushing handle

stainless steel screw

polypropene seat

steel frame

aluminium pushing pole

polythene bag

plastic brake

rubber tyre

2 Highlight the correct word in each pair of **bold** words.

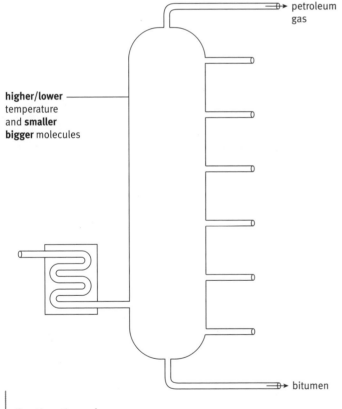

petroleum gas

higher/lower temperature and **smaller bigger** molecules

Fractionating column

bitumen

• **bigger/smaller** forces between molecules
• **easier/more difficult** for molecules to escape from liquid
• **higher/lower** boiling points

• **bigger/smaller** forces between molecules
• **easier/more difficult** for molecules to escape from liquid
• **higher/lower** boiling points

C 2

3 Read the article, then complete the tables below it by suggesting reasons for the scientists' observations and actions.

Gold nanoparticles kill cancer

Scientists have recently discovered that gold nanoparticles can kill cancer cells. They removed cancer cells from people with ear cancer, nose cancer, and throat cancer. They used chemicals to make gold nanoparticles enter the cancer cell nuclei.

The nucleus of a cancer cell divides more quickly than the nucleus of a normal cell. The scientists knew that if they could stop a cancer cell from dividing, they could stop the cancer. The scientists observed that, when gold nanoparticles entered a cell nucleus, the cell stopped dividing, and died.

In future, the scientists plan to test whether gold nanoparticles kill cancer cells when they are in the body. The scientists say they need to prevent gold nanoparticles entering healthy cells in the body.

Observation	Suggested reason
Nanometre-sized particles get into the nuclei of cancer cells more easily than normal-sized gold particles.	

Action	Suggested reason
The scientists tried to stop cancer cells dividing.	
The scientists did the tests on cancer cells outside the body.	
The scientists took cancer cells from many people.	
In future, when the scientists do tests on cancer cells inside the body, they will try to prevent gold nanoparticles entering healthy cells.	

4 Draw lines to match each modification to **one** diagram and **one or more** changes in property. Use each change in property once, more than once, or not at all.

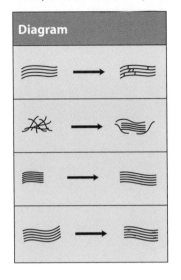

Diagram	Modification	Changes in properties
	increase chain length	stronger
		less flexible
	add plasticiser	softer
		harder
	make cross-links between polymer chains	more flexible
	pack molecules neatly together with crystalline regions	more dense
		less dense

5 Write a C in the boxes next to the equations for combustion reactions.
Write a P in the boxes next to the equations for polymerisation reactions.

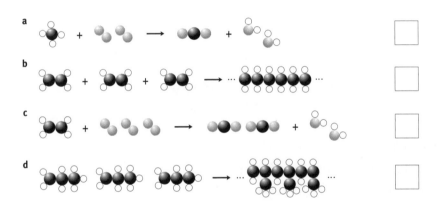

a

b

c

d

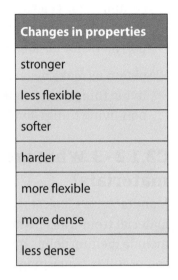

Key :
● = carbon atom
○ = hydrogen atom
● = oxygen atom

6 For each equation, draw more oxygen, carbon dioxide, or water molecules in the box so that there are the same number of atoms of each element in the products and reactants.

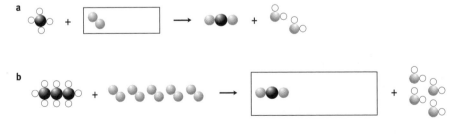

a

b

c

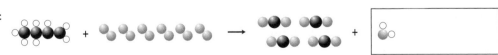

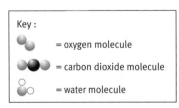

Key :
● = oxygen molecule
●●● = carbon dioxide molecule
○● = water molecule

C2.2.1–2 What are materials made from?

Every material is a chemical or mixture of chemicals, including:
- ceramics, for bricks, wall tiles, and plates
- metals, for vehicles, high-rise buildings, and jewellery
- polymers, for packaging and protective clothing.

We obtain or make materials from:
- living things, for example cotton, wool, leather, and wood
- non-living things, for example limestone and oil.

C2.1.2–3 What are the properties of materials?

Manufacturers look at materials' properties to choose the best material from which to make a product. Important properties include melting point, strength in tension (pulling), strength in compression (squashing), stiffness, hardness, and density.

The effectiveness and **durability** of a product depend on the properties of its materials. A product that is durable lasts for a long time before breaking or rotting.

C2.2.7 What's in crude oil?

Crude oil is a thick, dark-coloured liquid. It is mainly a mixture of **hydrocarbon** molecules of different lengths.

Hydrocarbon molecules are made from hydrogen and carbon only, for example propane and octane.

propane

octane

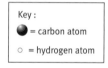

Key :
- ● = carbon atom
- ○ = hydrogen atom

C2.2.9–11 How is crude oil used?

Crude oil is not much use as it is. So oil companies use **fractional distillation** to separate crude oil into **fractions**. A fraction is a mixture of hydrocarbons with similar boiling points.

Fractional distillation happens in a fractionating tower. It works like this:
- Crude oil is heated in a furnace. Its compounds evaporate and become gases.
- The gases enter the tower. As they move up, they cool down. Different fractions condense at different levels:
  - Compounds with small molecules have low boiling points. This is because the forces between the molecules are weak, so only a little energy is needed for them to break out of a liquid and form a gas. These molecules rise to the top of the tower.
  - Compounds with big molecules have higher boiling points. They condense at the bottom of the tower.

Different fractions have different uses, including:

- fuels, e.g. methane, petrol, diesel, and liquefied petroleum gas
- lubricants, e.g. Vaseline and engine oil
- raw materials to make new materials in **chemical synthesis**.

C2.2.3–6, C2.2.8, C2.2.12–13 How are polymers made?

Most of the chemicals obtained from crude oil are used as fuels. Just 4% of crude oil makes **synthetic materials**, such as polymers. Synthetic materials do not occur naturally. They are made in chemical processes from raw materials from the Earth.

Polymers are very long molecules. They form when many small molecules, called **monomers**, join together. This type of chemical reaction is called **polymerisation**.

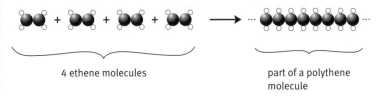

| 4 ethene molecules | part of a polythene molecule |

In polymerisation reactions – as in all chemical reactions – there are the same numbers of atoms of each element in both the reactants and products. The atoms are **rearranged**.

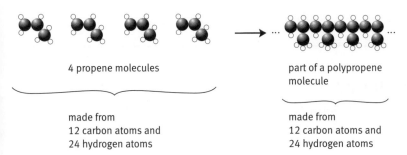

4 propene molecules

part of a polypropene molecule

made from
12 carbon atoms and
24 hydrogen atoms

made from
12 carbon atoms and
24 hydrogen atoms

There are many polymers, all made from different starting materials. Each polymer has unique properties.

Synthetic polymers have replaced natural materials in many products. For example, many ropes are now made with polypropene instead of sisal. Clothes may be made from nylon instead of cotton, because nylon is more durable.

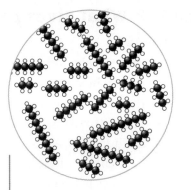

Crude oil is a mixture of hundreds of different hydrocarbons.

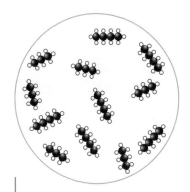

These molecules go right to the top of the fractionating column. This fraction contains some of the shortest hydrocarbons. There are weak forces between the molecules, giving them a low boiling point.

C2

> **Exam tip**
>
> Remember, the bigger the molecule, the higher the boiling point.

C2.3.1–3 What gives polymers their properties?

The properties of polymers depend on how their molecules are arranged and held together. For example, wax has shorter molecules than polythene. This means that:

- Polythene is stronger, since its long molecules are tangled and difficult to separate.
- Polythene melts at higher temperatures since there are stronger forces between long polythene molecules than between shorter wax molecules.

C2.3.4 What makes polymer properties change?

Method	How properties change	Diagram
making chains longer	• stronger	
adding cross-links	• harder • stronger • less flexible	
adding plasticisers	• softer • more flexible	
increasing crystallinity by lining up polymer molecules	• stronger • denser	

C2.4.1–6 What is nanotechnology?

Nanotechnology is the use and control of tiny structures. **Nanoparticles** are about the same size as some molecules, between about 1 and 100 nanometres (nm) across.

Nanoparticles have different properties compared with larger particles of the same material. This is partly because nanoparticles have a bigger surface area compared with their volume.

Nanoparticles can occur:

- naturally, in sea spray
- by accident, when fuels burn
- by design, for example:
  - silver nanoparticles give fibres antibacterial properties, in medical dressings and socks
  - adding nanoparticles to plastics for sports equipment such as tennis rackets makes them stronger.

Nanoparticles may have harmful effects on health. Some people think these effects should be studied more closely before using nanoparticles more widely.

Use extra paper to answer these questions if you need to.

1   Tick the boxes to show which materials listed below are obtained or made from living things.

a   cotton ☐   d   wool ☐

b   copper ☐   e   paper ☐

c   limestone ☐   f   silk ☐

2   Highlight the statements below that are **true**. Then write corrected versions of the statements that are **false**.

a   A synthetic material is one that is obtained from living things.

b   A hydrocarbon is a compound made of carbon, hydrogen, and oxygen only.

c   In a polymerisation reaction, small molecules join together to make very long molecules.

d   Monomers are very long molecules.

e   Most crude oil is used for chemical synthesis.

f   In a chemical reaction, there are always more atoms of each element in the product than in the reactants.

3   Choose words or phrases from the box to fill in the gaps in the sentences below. The words in the box may be used once, more than once, or not at all.

molecules	NM	100	atoms	seaspray
10000	fuel combustion products			
grains of sand	1	10	nm	nM	Nm

Nanotechnology involves structures that are about the same size as some _____ . Nanoparticles have diameters of between _____ and _____ nanometres. Nanometre is also written as _____ . Nanoparticles can occur by accident in _____ . They also occur naturally in _____ . Scientists also make nanoparticles.

4   The table shows the properties of two materials used to make dental fillings. Use the data in the table to suggest why many people now prefer polymer fillings, even though amalgam fillings have been used for many more years.

Property	Amalgam	Dental polymer
Conduction of heat	good conductor of heat	poor conductor of heat
Colour	silver	white
Risks	contains mercury, which is poisonous	no known health risks

5   The table shows the properties of two materials: polypropene and sisal.

Property	Polypropene	Sisal
durability	does not rot	rots
colour	can be pigmented any colour	can be dyed any colour
relative strength in tension	1.4	0.8
flexibility	very flexible	very flexible

Ropes for life buoys near rivers used to be made from sisal. Now they are made from polypropene. Select data from the table to suggest two reasons that explain why polypropene is now preferred for making life buoy ropes.

6   The table shows the properties of two polymers, LDPE and HDPE. Use data from the table to explain why HDPE is the better polymer for making garden furniture.

Property	LDPE	HDPE
density (g/cm³)	0.92	0.95
maximum temperature at which the polymer can be used (°C)	85	120
strength (MPa)	12	31
relative flexibility	flexible	stiff

7   Highlight the correct word or phrase in each pair of **bold** words.

Kerosene and petrol are two **fractions/polymers** obtained by the fractional distillation of crude oil. The hydrocarbon molecules in kerosene are bigger than those in petrol. So the forces of attraction between molecules in kerosene are **greater/smaller** than those in petrol. This means that the hydrocarbons in kerosene have **lower/higher** boiling points than those in petrol. Kerosene is removed from **lower down/higher up** the fractionating tower.

8   Give one reason to explain why nanoparticles of a material may show different properties compared with larger particles of the same materials.

9   Give two examples of how nanoparticles are used.

10 Suggest why some people are concerned about the widespread use of products containing nanoparticles.

H 11 For each of the changes listed below, describe the effect it has on the properties of a polymer, and explain why it has this effect. Include diagrams to help you explain your answer.

a   increased chain length   c   adding plasticisers

b   cross-linking   d   increasing crystallinity

C 2

1 The table shows the properties of some synthetic polymers.

Letter	Name of material	Properties
A	poly(2-hydroxyethylmethacrylate) (PHEMA)	transparent; absorbs water to become flexible and jelly-like
B	acrylic	easily moulded into shape
C	polyethenol	flexible, soluble in water
D	silicone rubber	insoluble in water; very durable

a Study the properties of the materials in the table. Choose the best material to make each of the following items. Write the letter of one material next to each item.

artificial heart valves ☐

hospital laundry bags that dissolve in a washing machine, allowing dirty sheets to be washed without needing to be handled ☐

part of a composite used to make fillings for front teeth ☐

contact lenses ☐ [4]

b Disposable nappies are made from several materials, including:

cellulose   polypropene   polythene

i From the list above, write the name of one material that is obtained from a living thing.

_____ [1]

ii Draw rings round the properties that the outermost layer of a disposable nappy must have.

**non-toxic   hard   flexible
high strength in tension   stiff** [2]

iii Polythene is made when small molecules join together to make very long molecules. Give the name of this process.

_____ [1]

Total [8]

2 A student wants to make a one-person rowing boat to use on a lake.

He investigates three materials.
He does experiments to obtain the data in the first two lines of the table on the next page.

He uses the Internet to collect the data in the last two lines of the table.

Property	Aluminium alloy 5083	ABS steel (an alloy of iron)	Glass-reinforced plastic
Mass (g)	30.5	115.0	20.7
Volume (cm³)	11.5	16.2	14.8
Density (g/cm³)			
Tensile strength (MPa) (the force to pull a material until it breaks)	300	between 400 and 490	varies, but lower than aluminium and steel
Yield strength (MPa) (how much a material bends before it won't spring back into shape)	150	235	low – the material is brittle and shatters easily on collision

a Use the equation below to calculate the density of each material in the table.

Write your answers in the empty boxes in the table.

density = mass ÷ volume [3]

b Use all the data in the table, including your calculated density values, to choose the best material for the rowing boat. Give reasons for your choice.

_____

_____

_____

_____ [4]

Total [7]

C 2

3 The table gives data about three building materials.

Material	Compressive strength, in MPa (how much pushing force the material can withstand before it is crushed)	Thermal conductivity, in W/mK (how well the material conducts heat – the bigger the number, the better the material conducts heat)
Limestone	60	1.3
High strength concrete	60	1.7
Wood (oak)	15	0.1

Use only the data in the table to evaluate the advantages and disadvantages of using the three materials listed in the table to build a house.

The quality of written communication will be assessed in your answer to this question.

Write your answer on separate paper or in your exercise book.

Total [6]

4 a The chemicals used to make candle wax and shoe polish are obtained from crude oil.

- Candle wax is made from hydrocarbon chains that are about 30 carbon atoms long.
- The waxy ingredient of shoe polish is made from hydrocarbon chains that are about 70 carbon atoms long.

Tick the **two statements that best explain** why shoe polish wax has a higher melting point than candle wax.

The forces between long hydrocarbon molecules are stronger than the forces between short hydrocarbon molecules. ☐

The forces between long hydrocarbon molecules are weaker than the forces between short hydrocarbon molecules. ☐

The stronger the forces between molecules, the smaller the amount of energy needed to separate them. ☐

The stronger the forces between molecules, the more energy is needed to separate them. ☐ [2]

b i PVC is a polymer. It is used to make these items:
- window frames
- floor coverings
- shower curtains

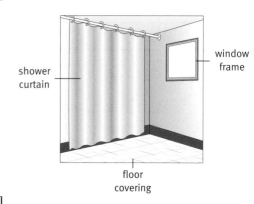

Write the name of the item that has the most plasticiser added to the PVC that it is made from.

_____

Give a reason for your choice.

_____ [2]

ii Rubber is used to make car tyres and elastic bands.

Predict which has more cross-linking: the rubber in car tyres or the rubber in elastic bands.

_____

Give a reason for your choice.

_____ [2]

Total [6]

P2 Radiation and life

1 Use the words in the box to finish labelling the diagram.

detector	energy of each photon	intensity	absorbs
number of photons	transmits	reflects	source

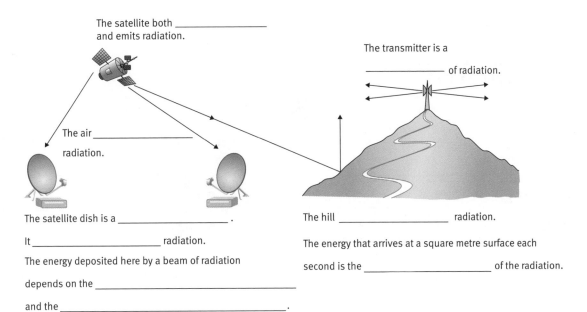

The satellite both _____ and emits radiation.

The transmitter is a _____ of radiation.

The air _____ radiation.

The satellite dish is a _____ .

It _____ radiation.

The energy deposited here by a beam of radiation depends on the _____

and the _____ .

The hill _____ radiation.

The energy that arrives at a square metre surface each second is the _____ of the radiation.

2 Solve the clues to fill in the grid.

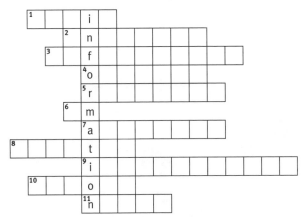

1 Signals are carried through space and the Earth's atmosphere by microwaves and _____ waves.

2 Signals are carried through optical fibres by light waves and _____ rays.

3 The more _____ stored, the better the quality of an image or sound.

4 Light and infrared carry information along _____ fibres.

5 A radio _____ decodes a radio wave's pattern of variation to reproduce the original sound.

6 The signal carried by FM and _____ radio waves varies in exactly the same way as the information from the original sound wave.

7 The signal carried by FM waves is called an _____ signal.

8 Sound waves can be converted into a _____ code made of two signals.

9 Analogue and digital signals pick up random unwanted signals as they travel. This is called _____, or noise.

10 Digital radio receivers pick up pulses and _____ them to make a copy of the original sound wave.

11 Digital radio receivers clean up signals to remove _____.

3 Add captions to each picture. Use a separate sheet of paper if there is not enough space for you to write in the boxes. Include:

- the name of the type of electromagnetic radiation represented (radio waves, ultraviolet radiation, and so on)
- the damage (if any) this type of radiation can do to living cells
- what Alex can do to protect himself from this type of radiation (if he needs to do anything).

Alex's holiday: a day in the life

3 Is that the dentist? My filling's just fallen out.

P2.1.1 What is electromagnetic radiation?

Electromagnetic radiation travels as waves. It carries energy.

- A **source** gives out radiation.
- The radiation spreads out from its source'
- The radiation may be **reflected**, **transmitted**, or **absorbed**.
- Some of the radiation may be absorbed by a **detector**.

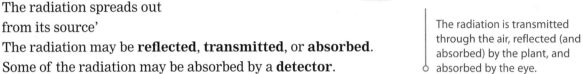

journey

absorbing material in retina of eye, the **detector**

reflecting material

The radiation is transmitted through the air, reflected (and absorbed) by the plant, and absorbed by the eye.

P2.1.3, P2.1.7–9 How much energy does radiation transfer?

Electromagnetic radiation transfers energy in packets, or **photons**. The amount of energy absorbed by a detector depends on:

- the number of photons
- the amount of energy each photon carries.

The amount of energy that arrives at a square metre of a surface each second is the **intensity** of the radiation.

As it gets further from its source, the intensity of a beam of electromagnetic radiation decreases.

This is because, as it spreads out, the radiation reaches bigger and bigger surface areas. Also, some of the radiation is absorbed by the medium it is travelling through.

P2.1.2, P2.1.4–6 What is the electromagnetic spectrum?

The electromagnetic spectrum includes these radiations:

| radio waves | microwaves | infrared | visible light | ultraviolet | X-rays | gamma rays |

increasing frequency →

All types of electromagnetic radiation travel at 300 000 km/s through a vacuum. The photons of high frequency waves carry more energy than the photons of low frequency waves.

P2.1.10–12 What happens when materials absorb radiation?

When materials absorb electromagnetic radiation, they gain energy.

- Radio waves and microwaves cause a varying electric current in a metal wire, such as a radio or phone aerial.

P2

> **Exam tip**
>
> Learn the order of the radiations in the diagram – you might be asked about it in an exam.

- Microwaves and infrared waves heat materials.
- Ultraviolet radiation, X-rays, and gamma rays have enough energy to change atoms and molecules.

  ⊕ This may lead to chemical reactions, such as photosynthesis and those that happen in the retina of your eye.
- Photons of ultraviolet radiation, X-rays, and gamma rays can carry enough energy to remove an electron from an atom or molecule. This is **ionisation**.

P2.2.1–4 Do microwaves harm humans?

Microwaves, light, and infrared radiation can heat materials by making their particles vibrate faster. This **heating effect** depends on the radiation's intensity and the length of time it is absorbed.

The heating effect can damage cells. Some people think that low intensity microwave radiation from mobile phone handsets is a risk to health. Others say the evidence does not support this claim.

Some microwaves are strongly absorbed by water. They are used for cooking water-containing foods in microwave ovens. Microwave ovens have metal cases and door screens that reflect or absorb microwaves to stop them leaving the oven.

P2.2.6–7 What damage do gamma rays do?

Radioactive materials emit gamma radiation all the time. This ionising radiation damages the DNA of living cells. The damage may lead to cancer or cell death.

P2.2.8–10 What protects us from UV?

The Sun emits ultraviolet radiation (UV). This can cause skin cancer.

A layer of gases in the atmosphere – the **ozone layer** – protects living organisms by absorbing most of the UV radiation from the Sun. People use sun-screens and clothes to absorb harmful UV radiation that gets through the ozone layer.

⊕ When ozone absorbs UV radiation, its molecules break down.

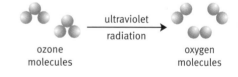

ozone molecules → ultraviolet radiation → oxygen molecules

P2.2.11 How are X-rays useful?

X-rays are absorbed by dense materials, but pass through less dense ones. This means they are used to produce:
- shadow pictures of bones in our bodies
- shadow pictures of objects in luggage at airports.

People who work with X-rays are protected from radiation by dense materials such as lead and concrete.

P2.3.1–4 How does electromagnetic radiation make life possible?

All objects emit electromagnetic radiation. The **principal frequency** of the radiation emitted by an object is the frequency that is emitted with the highest intensity. The higher the temperature of an object, the higher its principal frequency.

P2.3.5–11 What is the greenhouse effect?

Greenhouse gases keep the Earth warmer than it would otherwise be. There are three main greenhouse gases in the atmosphere:

- carbon dioxide (the most important greenhouse gas, present in small amounts compared to other atmospheric gases)
- methane (trace amounts)
- water vapour.

The concentration of carbon dioxide in the atmosphere hardly changed for thousands of years. The carbon dioxide removed by photosynthesis was balanced by that returned by respiration. There is a diagram of the carbon cycle on page 74.

Since 1800 the concentration of carbon dioxide increased, mainly because humans:

- burn increasing amounts of fossil fuels
- cut down and burn forests to clear land.

Computer climate models provide evidence that human activities are causing global warming.

Global warming may lead to:

- climate change, meaning that some food crops will no longer grow in some places
- ice melting and seawater expanding as it warms up, causing rising sea levels and flooding of low-lying land
- more extreme weather conditions
  because higher temperatures cause more convection in the atmosphere, and more evaporation of water from oceans and the land.

P2.4.1–2 How does radiation carry information?

Electromagnetic waves travel from a source to a detector. We can use them to transmit information.

- Microwaves, and some radio waves, are not strongly absorbed by the atmosphere. They carry information for radio and TV programmes through the air.
- Visible light and infrared radiation are not absorbed by glass. They carry information along optical fibres for cable TV and high-speed Internet connections.

P2

We send information from place to place using a **carrier wave**. The carrier wave is the radio wave, microwave, visible light, or infrared radiation. Adding information to the carrier wave creates a signal.

P2.4.3–7 Analogue or digital?

An **analogue signal** changes all the time. For example FM and AM radio waves vary in the same way as the information from the original sound wave.

A **digital signal** can take just two values. Its code is made up of two symbols, 0 and 1. The coded information is carried by switching the carrier wave on and off. This makes short bursts of waves, or **pulses**:

- 0 = no pulse
- 1 = pulse.

When a radio, mobile phone, or computer receives the waves, a processor in the device decodes the pulses. This converts the digital signal back to the original analogue signal.

The advantages of digital signals include:

- the information can be stored and processed by microprocessors in computers and phones
- digital information can be stored in small memories.

As analogue and digital signals travel, they pick up unwanted electrical signals. This is **noise**, or **interference**. It is easier to remove noise from a digital signal than an analogue one. This is because, for digital signals, 0 and 1 can still be recognised if noise has been picked up. The signal can be 'cleaned up' by removing the noise. Noise cannot be removed from analogue signals.

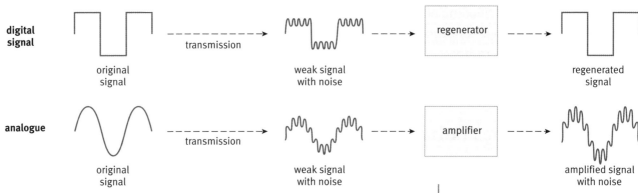

After transmission, a signal is weaker and noisier than the original. A digital signal can be 'cleaned up' by a regenerator.

P2.4.10–11 How is information stored?

The amount of information needed to store an image or sound is measured in bytes (B). The more information stored, the better the quality of the image or sound.

Use extra paper to answer these questions if you need to.

1   Write each type of electromagnetic radiation below in the correct column of a copy of the table.
    a   high energy ultraviolet   d   infrared
    b   light   e   gamma rays
    c   X-rays   f   microwaves

Ionising radiations	Radiations that cause a heating effect only

2   Write the letters of the radiations below in order of increasing frequency.
    A   X-rays   E   gamma rays
    B   infrared   F   ultraviolet
    C   visible   G   radio waves
    D   microwaves

3   Write the letter C next to the statements that are true for carbon dioxide. Write the letter O next to the statements that are true for ozone. Write B next to statements that are true for both.
    a   This gas is added to the atmosphere by respiration.
    b   This gas absorbs ultraviolet radiation.
    c   This gas is present in the Earth's atmosphere.
    d   This gas helps to prevent people getting skin cancer.
    e   This gas is removed from the atmosphere by photosynthesis.
    f   The amount of this gas in the atmosphere is increasing.

4   Highlight the statements below that are **true**. Write a correct version of the false statement.
    a   The higher the frequency of an electromagnetic radiation, the less energy is transferred by each photon.
    b   Ionising radiation removes electrons from atoms or molecules.
    c   Metals reflect microwaves.

5   Use the words in the box to fill in the gaps. Each word can be used once, more than once, or not at all.

radio	light	absorbed	reflected	TV
	microwaves	infrared	transmitted	

Radio waves and _____ carry information for _____ and _____ because they are not strongly _____ by the atmosphere. _____ and _____ carry information along optical fibres because the radiation is not _____ much by glass.

6   Which picture (X, Y, or Z) has the best quality image? Explain how you know. All three pictures are printed the same size.

Picture	Amount of information
X	1 Mb
Y	100 kB
Z	10 kB

7   Draw lines to match each wave to its description.

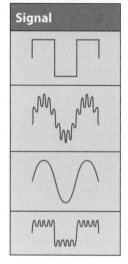

Signal	Description
	a digital signal without noise
	an analogue signal without noise
	a digital signal with noise
	an analogue signal with noise

8   This question is about the greenhouse effect.
    a   Name two natural processes that add carbon dioxide to the atmosphere.
    b   Name one natural process that removes carbon dioxide from the atmosphere.
    c   Explain why the amount of carbon dioxide in the atmosphere has been increasing over the past 200 years.
    d   Name two greenhouse gases, other than carbon dioxide.
    e   List three possible effects of global warming.

9   Name substances that absorb each of the following types of radiation:
    a   microwaves
    b   ultraviolet radiation
    c   X-rays.

H 10 Write a definition for the **intensity** of a beam of electromagnetic radiation.

11 Explain why the intensity of a beam of electromagnetic radiation decreases with distance from the source.

12 Write the formula of an ozone molecule and an oxygen molecule. Describe what happens when an ozone molecule absorbs ultraviolet radiation.

13 Explain what the term **principal frequency** means. Which has a higher principal frequency – the Earth or the Sun?

14 Explain why global warming could result in more extreme weather events.

P 2

1 The diagram shows part of the carbon cycle.

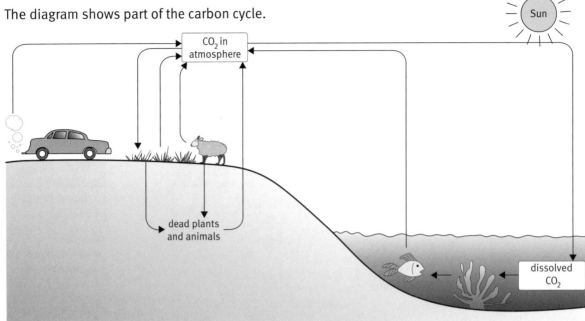

a **i** Name two processes that add carbon dioxide to the atmosphere.

_____ [2]

ii Name two processes that remove carbon dioxide from the atmosphere.

_____ [2]

b Increasing amounts of carbon dioxide in the atmosphere cause global warming.

i Give two problems caused by global warming.

_____

_____ [2]

ii Name two greenhouse gases other than carbon dioxide.

_____ [2]

Total [8]

2

Scientists have invented a scanner to find out if premature babies are at risk of brain damage.

The scanner sends beams of light into the brain. It uses light of two wavelengths: 780 nm and 815 nm.

Some of the light passes through brain tissue. Some of the light is absorbed by water in the brain. Most of the light is scattered in all directions.

Detectors in the scanner measure the intensity of the light that comes out of the brain. If the intensity is less than expected, the baby's brain might be bleeding.

The scanner builds up a 3-dimensional image o the brain.

Doctors can use this to find out where the bleeding is.

a What scientific word means that light **passes through** brain tissue?

Draw a (ring) around the correct answer.

transmitted   reflected   absorbed   [1]

b Use the information in the box to decide whether blood transmits, reflects, or absorbs the light that the scanner emits.

Draw a (ring) around the correct answer.

transmits   reflects   absorbs   [1]

Give a reason for your decision.

_____

_____

_____

_____   [2]

c The diagram shows some of the detectors around a baby's head.

Each detector records a different reading for light intensity.
Why are the readings different?
Tick the **best** answer.

The amount of energy carried by a photon
does not change.   ☐

In one second, a different number of photons
arrives at each detector.   ☐

The amount of energy carried by a photon
changes each second.   ☐

Each photon carries the same amount
of energy.   ☐   [1]

P2

d i Give one reason why it would not be sensible for the scanner to send X-rays into the brain.

_____   [1]

ii Give one reason why it would not be sensible for the scanner to send microwaves into the brain.

_____   [1]

Total [7]

3 Methane and carbon dioxide are greenhouse gases.

✎ The quality of written communication will be assessed in your answer to this question.

Write your answer on separate paper or in your exercise book. Use evidence from the five graphs below to identify and evaluate evidence for global warming, and its causes and effects.

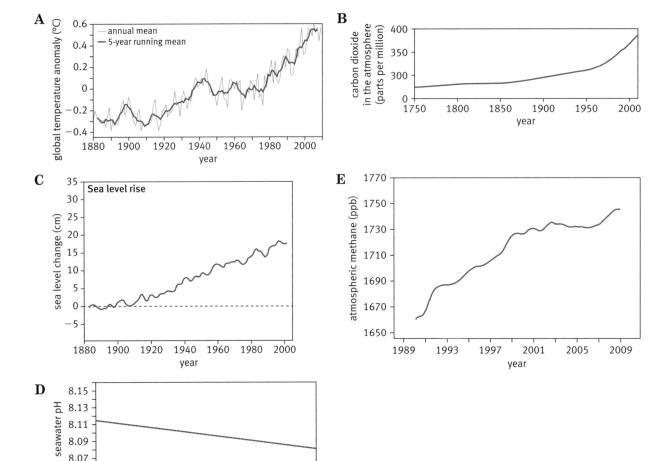

Total [6]

4 Beams of electromagnetic radiation from the phone mast deliver photons ('packets') of energy to Mike's and Helen's mobile phones.

The amount of energy delivered by each photon is the same. Explain why the amount of energy that arrives at Helen's mobile phone is less than the amount of energy that arrives at Mike's mobile phone.

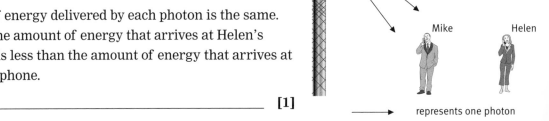

_____ **[1]**

Total [1]

1 Make notes about energy transfer between organisms in the box below. Two of the rows have been filled in for you.
   - Write the title in the top row.
   - Write the most important point (the key idea) in the next row down.
   - Write other relevant information in the lower rows.

Title	
Most important point (key idea)	Energy is transferred between organisms when a consumer eats another organism.
Other information	When a consumer eats a plant or animal, only some of the energy is transferred from the plant or animal to the consumer.

2 Do this activity with a friend.

Choose a box from the grid below.

Define the word at the top of the box. Do not use the 'taboo' word.

Get your friend to guess the word you are defining.

Non-living indicators	**Mutations**	**Genetic variation**
Taboo words:	*Taboo words:*	*Taboo words:*
• nitrate levels	• genes	• characteristics
• temperature	• changes	• inherited
• carbon dioxide levels	• inherited	• DNA
Competition	**Kingdom**	**Decomposers**
Taboo words:	*Taboo words:*	*Taboo words:*
• nutrients	• classification	• bacteria
• water	• group	• dead animals
• survival	• animal	• dead plants
Biodiversity	**Sustainability**	**Species**
Taboo words:	*Taboo words:*	*Taboo words:*
• variety	• needs	• breed
• species	• future	• offspring
	• environment	• fertile

3 This question is about the carbon cycle.

  a Look at the words in the box.

> atmosphere   photosynthesis   combustion
>
> fossil fuels   respiration   eating
>
> dying   decomposing

- Write an **s** next to each word that is a carbon store.
- Write a p next to each word that describes a process.

  b Write each word in the box above in the correct place on the carbon cycle opposite.

Write the carbon stores in the boxes.

Write process words next to arrows. One arrow does not need a label. You will need to use some process words more than once.

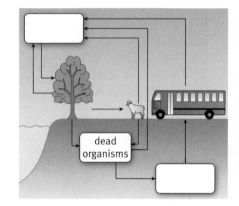

dead organisms

4

The Latin name of one woodlouse species is *Porcellio scaber*.

Woodlice are in these groups:
- invertebrates
- crustaceans
- Animal Kingdom.

Use the information in the box to fill in the gaps below.

The group with the largest number of organisms is the

_____ . The group containing organisms with

the smallest number of characteristics in common is the

_____ . Organisms in the same _____ can

breed to produce _____ offspring. Within a species,

there are fewer organisms with many _____ in

common.

> **Exam tip**
>
> You need to remember what *kingdoms* and *species* are. You will not be expected to remember the names of other types of groups.

B3.1.1–3 What are adaptations?

A **species** is a group of organisms that can breed together to produce **fertile** offspring.

Living organisms have features that help them survive in their environments. These are **adaptations**. Adaptations increase a species' chance of survival by making it more likely that individuals will survive and reproduce.

B3.1.4–8 How do species interact?

Within a place where an organism lives – its **habitat** – there is **competition** for resources. Animal species may compete for food or shelter. Plants compete for space and light.

Species in a habitat rely on each other, and on their environment, for food and other needs. The species are **interdependent**. A **food web** shows what eats what in a habitat.

Changes to the food web affect other species. The fox population may decrease. The populations of mice, slugs, beetles, and frogs then may increase. Badger numbers may increase because there are fewer foxes to compete with.

B3.1.9–11 How do plants use energy from the Sun?

Plants absorb 1–3% of the light energy from the Sun that falls on their leaves. They use this energy for **photosynthesis**. This produces the chemicals that make up plant cells and store energy. Plants are **producers**.

Animals, bacteria, and fungi depend on plants for food. So nearly all life is dependent on energy from the Sun

B3.1.12–14 How is energy transferred?

Energy is transferred between organisms:
*   when animals (**consumers**) eat other organisms
*   when decay organisms (**decomposers** and **detritivores**) eat dead organisms and waste materials.

Only a small percentage of the energy at each stage of a food chain is passed on. The rest of the energy:
*   is used for life processes (e.g. moving and keeping warm)
*   escapes to the surroundings as heat
*   is excreted as waste and passed on to decomposers
*   cannot be eaten and is passed on to decomposers.

Because so much energy passes out of a food chain, food chains usually have no more than four species.

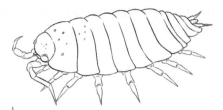

Woodlice live in dark damp places. Their adaptations help them to survive. Their colour makes it hard for predators to see them. Their external skeleton protects the soft parts of their body.

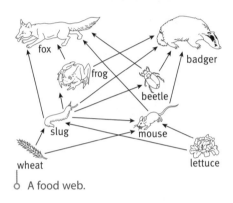

A food web.

B3

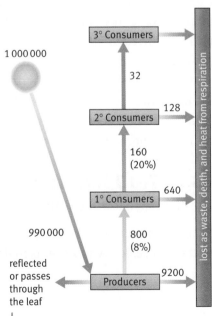

Energy flow through an ecosystem.

You can calculate the percentage efficiency of energy transfer at different stages of a food chain like this:

> In the food chain above, 32 units out of 160 units of energy are transferred from secondary consumers to tertiary consumers. So the percentage of the energy transferred is:
>
> $$\frac{32}{160} \times 100 = 20\%$$

B3.1.15–16 How is carbon recycled?

Carbon is recycled through the environment.

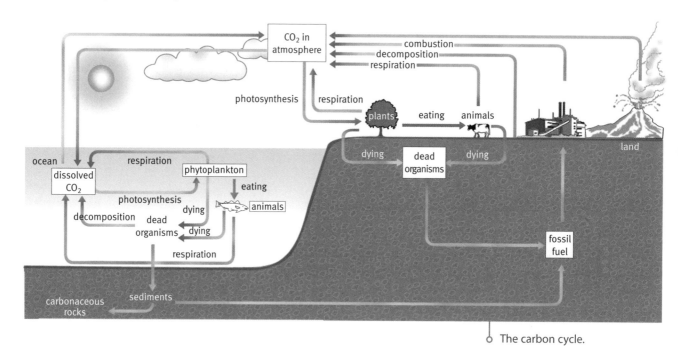

The carbon cycle.

Plants take carbon dioxide out of the atmosphere by **photosynthesis**. This makes glucose. Animals and plants break down glucose in **respiration**. This returns carbon dioxide to the atmosphere. Microorganisms break down the molecules of dead organisms by **decomposition**. The **combustion** of wood and fossil fuels adds carbon dioxide to the atmosphere.

Exam tip

Check the direction of arrows when looking at a carbon cycle. The arrows point to where the carbon atoms are going.

B3.1.17–19 How is nitrogen recycled?

The diagram shows how nitrogen is recycled in the environment.

Microorganisms are vital in the nitrogen cycle. **Decomposer bacteria** break down proteins in dead organisms.

The following processes are part of the nitrogen cycle:

- **Nitrogen-fixing bacteria** in some plant roots convert nitrogen into nitrogen compounds, including nitrates.
- Plants use nitrates to make proteins. Animals digest plant proteins and use them to make animal proteins.
- **Denitrifying bacteria** break down nitrates in the soil and release nitrogen to the air. This is **denitrification**.

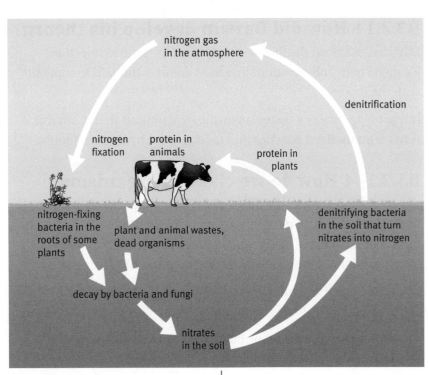

The nitrogen cycle

B3.1.20–22 Monitoring the environment

Scientists use indicators to measure environmental change. **Living indicators** include:

- phytoplankton, to measure ocean temperature changes
- lichens, to monitor air quality
- mayfly nymphs, to monitor oxygen levels in rivers.

Non-living indicators include:

- nitrate levels in streams, rivers, and lakes
- carbon dioxide levels and temperature in air and oceans.

B3.2.1–10 How has life evolved?

Life began about 3500 million years ago. All species evolved from simple living things. Fossils and DNA analysis of living organisms provide evidence for evolution.

There is **variation** between individuals of a species. **Genetic variation** is caused by **mutations** (changes to genes). Mutated genes in sex cells can be passed on to offspring. This occasionally produces new characteristics.

Over time, **evolution** makes species change. New species may develop, too. The changes below may cause evolution:

- mutations and **natural selection**
- environmental changes (some individuals have features that are better suited to a new environment)
- isolation (if a population of a species lives separately from another population of the same species, and changes).

Natural selection is different from **selective breeding**, in which humans choose characteristics for a plant or animal.

B3

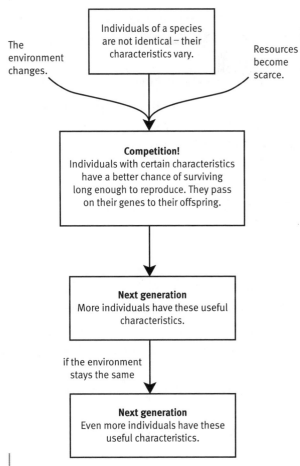

The flow chart shows how natural selection works.

B3.2.11 How did Darwin develop his theory?

Darwin developed the theory of evolution by natural selection. He made many observations and used creative thought to come up with the theory.

Darwin's theory is a better scientific explanation than Lamarck's. It fits with modern genetics and is supported by more evidence.

B3.3.1–4 How do we classify organisms?

There is a huge variety of life on Earth. Living organisms include plants, animals, and microorganisms. Within each of these groups there are millions of species. And within each species there is a much genetic variation. This variety is called **biodiversity**.

Scientists use the similarities and differences of organisms' physical features and DNA to put them into groups. This is **classification**.

Classifying organisms helps make sense of the diversity of life. It also helps to show how organisms have evolved.

Living things have Latin names. The cat is *Felis catus*. It is in these groups:

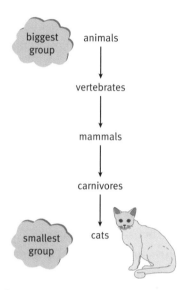

The biggest group that cats belong to is the **Animal Kingdom**. Organisms in the animal kingdom have only a few characteristics in common. The smallest group that cats are in is their species. Its members have many characteristics in common.

B3.3.5–9 Why does biodiversity matter?

Sustainability means meeting the needs of people today without damaging the Earth for people in future. Preserving biodiversity is a vital part of living sustainably:

- We use wild varieties of plant species to develop new varieties of food crops.
- We use plant substances as medicines.

Growing single crops in large fields (**monoculture**) is not sustainable. These crops can easily be attacked by pests and diseases. But crops with more varied alleles are likely to include some resistant plants.

B3.1.8 Why do species become extinct?

If all the members of a species die out, the species is **extinct**. Every year, more species become extinct. A species may become extinct if:

- there are changes in the environment to which a species cannot adapt
- a new species arrives that competes with, eats, or causes disease of the species
- another species in its food web becomes extinct.

B3.3.10–11 Why is packaging a problem?

The production and transport of packaging uses huge amounts of energy. Packaging also creates lots of waste. In landfill sites this waste takes up a lot of space. Biodegradable packaging often fails to decompose in landfill sites because there is not enough oxygen. It is more sustainable to reduce our use of packaging.

Use extra paper to answer these questions if you need to.

1 Write the letter N next to non-living indicators of environmental change. Write the letter L next to living indicators.

a nitrate levels

b lichens

c temperature

d mayfly nymphs

2 Draw lines to match each word to its definition.

Words	Definitions
variation	the place where an organism lives
mutations	everything around an organism, including air, water, and other living things
habitat	differences between organisms
environment	changes to genes

3 Choose words from the box to fill in the gaps. The words may be used once, more than once, or not at all.

> small   chemicals   dead   heat   warm
>
> large   materials   respiration   photosynthesis
>
> energy   moving   waste

Plants absorb a _____ percentage of the Sun's energy for _____ . This energy is stored in the _____ of plant cells. When one organism eats another, only about 10% of the _____ is transferred to the organism. This is because some of the energy is transferred in life processes such as _____ and keeping _____ , and some is transferred to the surroundings as _____ . Also, some energy remains in undigested _____ . In the same way, when decomposers feed on _____ organisms and waste _____ , only some of the energy is transferred to the decomposers.

4 Highlight the statements below that are **true**. Then write corrected versions of the statements that are **false**.

a Life on Earth began about 3500 billion years ago.

b Mutated genes in sex cells cannot be passed on to offspring.

c In selective breeding, humans choose individual plants or animals to breed from.

d Evolution is the process by which species gradually change over time.

5 Polar bears have thick white fur. They are good swimmers. Explain how these adaptations increase their chance of survival in the arctic.

6 The diagram below shows part of a food chain in Australia.

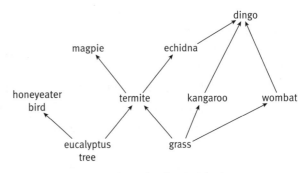

a Name the animals in the food web that eat grass.

b Name the producers in the food web.

c Name the primary consumers in the food web.

d Explain what might happen to the wombat population if the kangaroo population decreases.

e Explain what might happen to the honeyeater bird population if eucalyptus trees are cut down.

f Explain what might happen to the wombat population if dingoes die.

7 In the food chain below, there are 200 units of energy in all the herrings eaten by a shark. The amount of energy transferred to the shark is 28 units. Calculate the percentage of energy that is transferred.

phytoplankton ⟶ zooplankton ⟶ herring ⟶ shark

8 List three ways by which changes in the environment may cause a species to become extinct.

9 Explain why Darwin's theory of evolution by natural selection is a better theory than Lamarck's explanation of evolution.

Ⓗ 10 Explain the meaning of the word *interdependence*.

11 What is a detritivore?

12 Draw lines to link the name of each process in the nitrogen cycle to what it does.

Name of process	What it does
decay	breaks down nitrates to form nitrogen
nitrogen fixation	forms nitrates from nitrogen
excretion	breaks down proteins
denitrification	removes waste from an organism

B 3

1 Read the information in the box.

> Here is part of an Antarctic food web:
>
>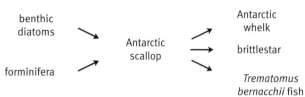
>
> Scientists have discovered that the sea temperature around Antarctica has risen by 1°C since 1960. Warmer sea water creates problems for animals that live on the seabed.

a i Use the food web to name one predator of the Antarctic scallop.

_____

ii If the Antarctic scallop population decreases, what is likely to happen to the populations of its predators?

_____ [2]

b Scientists fear that if Antarctic sea temperatures continue to rise, some species may become extinct.

Use the information in the box above to tick the **two most likely reasons** for the possible future extinction of the brittlestar.

Environmental conditions change. ☐

A new species that is a prey animal of the brittlestar is introduced to Antarctica. ☐

A living thing that is a predator of the brittlestar becomes extinct. ☐

A new species that is a predator of the brittlestar is introduced to Antarctica. ☐ [2]

Total [4]

2 Energy is transferred between organisms in a food chain. Describe and explain what happens to the energy at each stage of a food chain.

✎ The quality of written communication will be assessed in your answer to this question.

Write your answer on separate paper or in your exercise book.

Total [6]

3 Scientists have studied how the cat family evolved. They discovered that lions and domestic cats shared a common ancestor 10.8 million years ago.

a How might the scientists have obtained evidence to support their explanation?

Tick the two best answers.

studying fossils ☐

analysing the fur of cat ancestors ☐

analysing the DNA of modern cats, lions, and other species of the cat family ☐

analysing the blood of cat ancestors ☐ [2]

b i Complete this sentence.

Domestic cats and lions evolved partly as a result of a process called natural _____. [1]

ii The stages below explain how evolution made changes to one species: lions.

The stages are in the wrong order.

A More individuals in this generation had features that helped them survive in their new environment.

B Early lions migrated from Asia to Africa. Some individuals had features that helped them survive in the new environment.

C Individual lions are not identical; the species shows variation.

D These lions bred. They passed on their genes to their cubs.

Fill in the boxes to show the correct order. The first one has been done for you.

C			

[2]

Going for the highest grades

c The diagram shows scientists' ideas about when some species of the cat family began evolving from their common ancestor.

B
3

For example, the domestic cat and the ocelot last shared a common ancestor 8.0 million years ago.

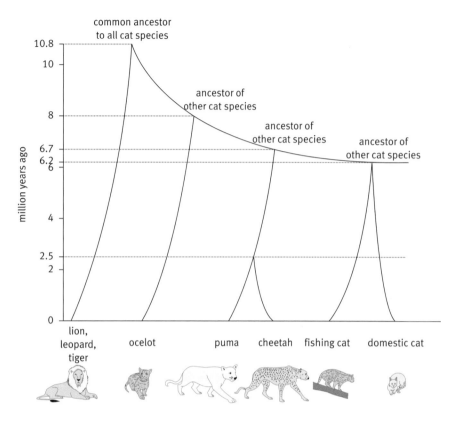

i When did the cheetah and the domestic cat last share a common ancestor?

_____ [1]

ii Which species on the chart probably has DNA that is most similar to that of the domestic cat?

_____ [1]

iii Read the information in the box opposite.

Complete the following sentences. Choose words from this list.

natural	**artificial**	**survival**
selection	**environmental**	**isolation**

This shows how _____ changes and

_____ help to produce new species.

Changes to genes (mutations) and _____

_____ also help to produce new

species. [3]

> The common ancestor of the puma and cheetah lived in North America. Individuals of the ancestor species migrated. Some went to South America and evolved into a new species: the puma. Others went to Africa and evolved to become a different species: the cheetah.

Total [10]

1   Decide which statements apply to chlorine, which statements apply to sodium chloride, and which statements apply to sodium hydroxide.

Write the letter of each statement in the correct part of the Venn diagram.

A   an element

B   a compound

C   includes chlorine atoms

D   dissolves in water to make an alkaline solution

E   obtained by solution mining

F   obtained from the sea

G   a chemical

H   includes sodium atoms

I   obtained by the electrolysis of brine

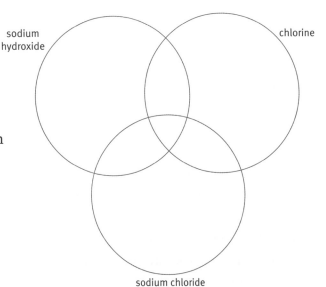

sodium hydroxide

chlorine

sodium chloride

2   Complete the table to summarise what geologists can find out from the clues.

Clue	What geologists can learn about a rock from this clue

Exam tip

Elements are made up of one type of atom. Compounds are made up of atoms of two or more elements, strongly joined together. The properties of a compound are very different to the properties of the elements it is made up of.

C 3

3 Annotate the diagram to explain how salt is obtained by solution mining.

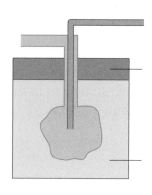

4 Solve the clues to fill in the grid.

1 An alkali reacts with fat to form …

2 When hydrogen chloride reacts with oxygen, it is …

3 Potassium … is an alkali.

4 The raw materials for making an alkali in the industrial revolution were salt, coal, and …

5 Pure sodium chloride is obtained from the sea and by … mining.

6 Scientists use … clues in rocks to track the past movements of continents.

7 The outer layer of the Earth is made up of … plates.

8 Two gases are obtained by the electrolysis of brine – chlorine and …

9 The food industry uses salt as a … and preservative.

10 PVC is made up of long chains of atoms, so it is a …

11 When added to water, … kills microorganisms.

12 Geologists get clues about the relative ages of rocks from …

13 Some synthetic chemicals are dangerous because they do not break down in the environment, so they travel long …

14 Eating too much salt can raise you blood …

C3.1.1–5, C3.1.7 How were rocks made?

The outer layer of the Earth is made up of about 12 **tectonic plates**. Convection currents under the plates make them move.

Scientists use magnetic clues in rocks like **magnetite** to track continents' movements. The movements mean that the parts of the ancient continents that now make up Britain have moved over the surface of the Earth. So different rocks, like salt, limestone, and coal, were formed in different climates.

These processes form rocks:

- **Sedimentation** and compression formed Peak District limestone when remains of dead sea animals fell to the bottom of warm seas near the equator.
- **Erosion** of rocks by rivers formed sand, which was deposited in layers to form sandstone.
- **Evaporation** formed rock salt when a sea moved inland, and its water evaporated. The salty water formed originally when salts from rocks dissolved in water flowing over them.
- **Mountain building** pushed coal towards the surface in the Peak District. The coal formed when tree ferns in swamps died, and were compressed and heated.

Chemical industries grew up where resources were available.

C3.1.6 How do we know how rocks were made?

Geologists study sedimentary rocks to find evidence of the conditions when they formed.

- Different animals lived at different times, so their **fossils** tell us about the ages of the rocks they are in
- Comparing **sand grains** in deserts and rivers to sand grains in sandstone tells us what sort of sand formed the sandstone
- The shapes of **ripples** in rocks give clues about whether sandstone was made from river bed sand or desert sand.
- Tiny **shell fragments** in limestone tell us about the conditions when the rock formed.

C3.2.1–5 Where does salt come from?

We use salt (sodium chloride) in food, to treat icy roads, and as a source of chemicals.

Salt for food must be pure. Some of it comes from the sea. The water evaporates, leaving salt behind. Countries with hot, dry climates get lots of salt from the sea, since energy costs are lower.

C 3

Rock salt is a mixture of salt and clay. It is used for de-icing roads, so need not be pure. It is mined from under the ground with big machines.

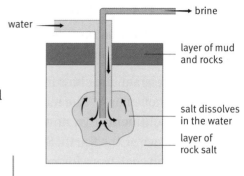

Extracting sodium chloride by solution mining

Salt for the chemical industry must be very pure. In Britain, it is obtained by solution mining. In solution mining, water is pumped into rock salt. Salt dissolves in the water underground. The salt solution is then pumped to the surface, and solid salt is extracted from the solution.

In the past, solution mining made huge underground holes. This caused **subsidence**, and buildings fell into the holes. Now, miners leave pillars in mines to prevent this problem.

C3.2.6–9 Why is salt added to food?

Salt is used by the food industry:
- as a **flavouring**, to improve the flavour of food
- as a **preservative**, to stop food going off.

Eating too much salt can raise your blood pressure. This increases the risk of having a stroke or heart attack.

Government departments do risk assessments on food chemicals like salt. They tell the public about the risks.

C3.3.1, C3.3.3–5 Why are alkalis useful?

Before industrialisation, alkalis were used to:
- neutralise acid soil
- make chemicals to bind dyes to cloth
- convert fats and oils into soap
- make glass.

Alkalis dissolve in water to make solutions with a pH above 7. They react with acids to form **salts**. The **word equation** shows how sodium hydroxide neutralises an acid.

sodium hydroxide + hydrochloric acid ⟶ sodium chloride + water

Alkalis include soluble hydroxides and soluble carbonates. Soluble hydroxides react with acids to form a salt and water:

sodium hydroxide + sulfuric acid ⟶ sodium sulfate + water

potassium hydroxide + nitric acid ⟶ potassium nitrate + water

Soluble carbonates react with acids to make a salt, water, and carbon dioxide:

sodium carbonate + hydrochloric acid ⟶ sodium chloride + water + carbon dioxide

> **Exam tip**
>
> Don't confuse sodium hydroxide (an alkali) with sodium chloride (common salt).

C3.3.2, C3.3.6–7 How were alkalis obtained?

Before the industrial revolution, people got alkalis from burnt wood and from stale urine.

In the industrial revolution, there was a shortage of alkali. A scientist invented a new way of making an alkali on a large scale. The raw materials were salt (sodium chloride), limestone (calcium carbonate), and coal.

The process made huge amounts of pollutants, including:
- acidic hydrogen chloride gas
- solid waste, which emitted toxic, smelly hydrogen sulfide gas.

In 1874, Henry Deacon worked out how to use one of the pollutants, hydrogen chloride, to make a useful product, chlorine. Hydrogen chloride is oxidised with oxygen:

$$\text{hydrogen chloride} + \text{oxygen} \longrightarrow \text{chlorine} + \text{water}$$

Hydrogen chloride is a compound. Its properties are different from those of the elements it is made up of, chlorine and hydrogen.

Chlorine is used as a bleach, and to whiten paper and textiles.

C3.3.10–13 Why add chlorine to water?

Sewage-contaminated water may contain microorganisms that cause cholera and typhoid. Chlorine kills the microorganisms. Adding chlorine to water leads to fewer deaths from waterborne diseases.

There may be disadvantages to chlorinating water. When chlorine reacts with **organic matter**, trihalomethanes (**THMs**) may form. Some people think that drinking this water can cause cancer.

C3.3.14–17 What does brine make?

Today, chlorine is made from sodium chloride solution (brine). Passing electricity through brine causes chemical changes. The elements in the sodium chloride (sodium and chlorine) and water (hydrogen and oxygen) are rearranged to make new products:
- chlorine gas – used to treat water, and to make bleach, plastics, and hydrochloric acid
- hydrogen gas – a fuel, and used to make hydrochloric acid
- sodium hydroxide solution – used to make soap, paper, and bleach.

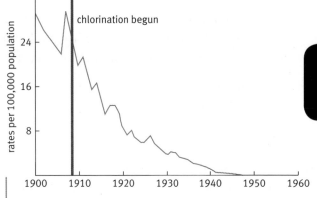

Death rate from typhoid fever in the USA, 1900–1960 (first published in the US Center for Disease Control and Prevention's Summary of Notifiable Diseases 1997).

Exam tip

Watch out! Chlorine becomes chloride in compounds like sodium chloride.

C
3

The electrolysis of brine needs electricity. If the electricity is generated from fossil fuels, much pollution results.

C3.4.1–2 Are chemicals risky?

Industry makes and uses many **synthetic chemicals**. In big quantities, some may harm health. But there is no evidence that the tiny amounts of these chemicals in human blood are unsafe.

For many chemicals, there are not enough data to judge whether the chemicals are likely to present a risk to health or the environment.

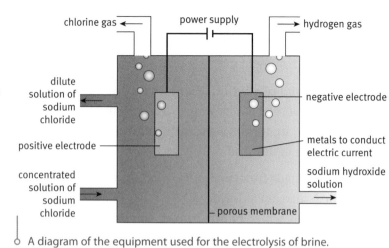

A diagram of the equipment used for the electrolysis of brine.

But there are twelve synthetic chemicals that are banned because everyone agrees are harmful, even in tiny amounts. These cause problems because:

- they do not break down in the environment
- they move long distances in the air and water
- they build up in fatty tissues of animals and humans.

C3.4.3–4 What are the dangers of PVC?

PVC is a useful synthetic chemical. It is a **polymer** – its molecules are made up of chains of carbon, hydrogen, and chlorine atoms.

Hard PVC makes window frames and underground water pipes. Softer PVC makes electric wire insulation, and clothing. PVC film makes hospital blood bags and drip bags.

PVC is softened by adding **plasticisers**. Plasticisers have small molecules. They can escape from the plastic and dissolve in liquids in contact with it. There is some evidence linking plasticisers to cancer and infertility. In the EU, some plasticisers have been banned from toys. PVC makers say plasticisers have never harmed anyone.

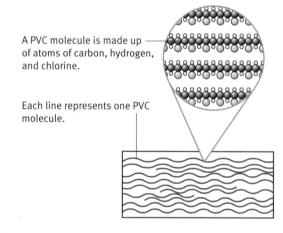

A PVC molecule is made up of atoms of carbon, hydrogen, and chlorine.

Each line represents one PVC molecule.

C3.4.5–6 What is a life cycle assessment?

We can use **life cycle assessments** (LCAs) to analyse the stages of the life of a product. LCAs include assessments of:

- the use of resources, including water
- the energy inputs or outputs
- the environmental impact.

Stage	Environmental impact
materials are made	raw materials to make material energy and water in processing
manufacturers make the product	materials to make product energy and water in manufacture
people use the product	energy to use product (e.g. petrol for a car) energy, water, and chemicals needed to maintain product
people get rid of the product	energy to take product away (fuel for bin lorry) space to store rubbish

Use extra paper to answer these questions if you need to.

1 Write an R next to the raw materials of the first industrial process for making sodium hydroxide (an alkali). Write a P next to the pollutants made in this process.

a coal   **d** limestone

b hydrogen sulfide   **e** salt

c hydrogen chloride

2 Draw lines to match each chemical to one or more of its uses.

Chemical
chlorine
sodium hydroxide
hydrogen
sodium chloride

Use
to de-ice roads
to make hydrochloric acid
to make soap
to preserve food
as a fuel
to make bleach

3 Highlight the one correct word or phrase in each pair of **bold** words or phrases.

PVC is a **plasticiser/polymer**. It is made up of **short/long** chains of atoms, including atoms of **carbon/sodium**. Hard PVC is used to make **window frames/wire insulation**. Soft PVC makes **window frames/wire insulation**. PVC is made soft by adding a **plasticiser/polymer**. This has **big/small** molecules, which can escape from the plastic. In the EU, some of these have been banned from **toys/clothes**.

4 Use the words in the box to fill in the gaps. Each word may be used once or more than once.

> materials   energy   discarded
>
>   chemicals   product

In a life cycle assessment, the first stage is to look at how the _____ are produced. Then assess the energy and water to make the _____ . Next, look at how much _____ and water are needed to use the product, and whether any _____ are needed to use or maintain it. Finally, consider what happens to the product when it is _____ . Can it be reused or recycled? How much _____ is needed to take it away?

5 Draw lines to match each process to a description of how it helps to form rock.

Process	How it helps form rock
sedimentation	formed sand, which deposited in layers to make sandstone
erosion	pushed coal nearer the surface
evaporation	with compression, formed limestone when dead sea creatures sank
mountain building	formed rock salt when a sea moved inland

6 The table shows the percentage of deaths in American cities from four diseases in 1900 and 1936. Chlorination of drinking water was introduced in many cities between 1900 and 1936.

Cause of death	Percentage of deaths in major cities	
	1900	1936
tuberculosis	11.1	5.3
pneumonia	9.6	9.3
typhoid	2.1	0.1
flu	0.7	1.3

a Which diseases caused a smaller percentage of deaths in 1936 than in 1900?

b From the data, can you conclude that adding chlorine to drinking water *caused* the reduction in the percentages of deaths from these diseases? Explain your decision.

7 Twelve synthetic chemicals, including DDT, are banned because everyone agrees they are harmful, even in small amounts. Give three reasons why they cause problems.

H 8 Name the products of the following reactions.

a sodium hydroxide and nitric acid

b potassium hydroxide and sulfuric acid

c potassium carbonate and hydrochloric acid

d sodium carbonate and sulfuric acid

e potassium hydroxide and hydrochloric acid

f sodium carbonate and nitric acid

9 Write word equations for each of the reactions in question 9.

C 3

1 This question is about the life cycle assessment (LCA) of a computer.

a Draw lines to link each activity to a stage in the life cycle of a computer.

Each stage in the life cycle may be linked to zero, one, or two activities.

Activity
putting together the computer components in its plastic case
recycling the computer components
extracting oil from wells beneath the sea
dismantling the computer
making plastics from oil

Stage in life cycle
Materials are produced.
Manufacturers make the computer.
People use the computer.
People throw away the computer.

[4]

b The data show the mass of carbon dioxide gas emissions during the manufacture of the different parts of a computer, and during its use.

Activity	Mass of carbon dioxide emissions (kg)
manufacture of flat screen	185
manufacture of electronic components	69
manufacture of chemicals used in computer	48
manufacture of plastic casing	17
manufacture of silicon wafers	15
manufacture of circuit boards	11
using the computer for one year	940

[Data from UNEP]

  i Calculate the total mass of carbon dioxide emissions for the manufacture of all the computer components listed in the table **and** for using the computer for one year.

Answer = _____ kg   [2]

  ii Calculate the total mass of carbon dioxide emissions for the manufacture of all the computer components listed in the table **and** for using the computer for five years.

Answer = _____ kg   [2]

  iii Give **two** reasons to explain why it is less damaging to the environment to use a computer for five years, than for one year, before replacing it with a new one.

_____

_____   [2]

c   This part of the question is about recycling computers.

i   It has been estimated that one tonne of waste from electronic products (including computers) contains about 225 g of the precious metals gold, silver, and palladium.

On average, there is about 170 g of these metals in one tonne of rock that contains these metals.

Describe **one benefit to the environment**, and **one benefit to people**, of using recycled precious metals in new computers, rather than getting the metals out of rocks from the ground.

_____

_____ [2]

ii   Read the article opposite, and then answer the question beneath it.

Identify one risk of dismantling old computers. Suggest why people do dismantle computers at the tip, even though there are risks in so doing.

_____

_____

_____ [2]

Total [14]

2   Describe three different methods by which alkalis have been manufactured in different stages of history.

Identify the advantages and disadvantages of each method.

✎ The quality of written communication will be assessed in your answer to this question.

Write your answer on separate paper or in your exercise book.

Total [6]

> **Illegal computer dumping risks lives**
>
> Some computers that have been sent for recycling are in fact shipped to poorer countries. Here they are dumped in huge tips.
>
> The waste contains hazardous materials, such as the beryllium used in circuit boards. Beryllium dust is toxic to humans. The element and its compounds can cause cancer.
>
> At the tips, people dismantle the computers and remove gold and other valuable metals.

C 3

3   The box gives the maximum daily amount of salt for children of different ages, recommended by the British Government.

a   Explain why the British Government gives recommendations for salt intake.

_____

_____ [1]

> 1 to 3 years old: 2 g of salt/day
> 4 to 6 years old: 3 g of salt/day
> 7 to 10 years old: 5 g of salt/day
> 11 years and older: 6 g of salt/day

b The table gives the amounts of salt in two products, made by the same company, to sell in different countries.

Country	Mass of salt in food (g)	
	100 g of bran cereal	One bacon double cheesebur
Canada	2.15	–
USA	0.65	–
Brazil	–	3.2
UK	1.13	2.1

i In which of the countries in the table is there the greatest mass of salt in bran cereal?

_____ [1]

ii Suggest two reasons to explain why the same manufacturer adds different amounts of salt to the same food in different countries.

_____

_____ [2]

iii Pedro is 16. He lives in Brazil.
In one day, he eats one bacon double cheeseburger at lunchtime, and one in the evening.
Calculate the total mass of salt in the burgers.

_____

_____ [1]

iv Compare the mass of salt in Pedro's burgers with the recommended daily maximum amount of salt for a 16-year-old.

What advice would you give Pedro?
Give reasons to support your answer.

_____

_____ [2]

Total [7]

> **Exam tip**
>
> When using data from tables, make sure you check the units and amounts given in the column headings.

🛈 Going for the highest grades

4 Predict the names of the products of the following reactions.

a copper carbonate with hydrochloric acid

_____ [2]

b sodium hydroxide with nitric acid

_____ [2]

c potassium hydroxide with sulfuric acid

_____ [2]

Total [6]

P3 Sustainable energy

1 Write each letter in an appropriate box to summarise some different ways of generating electricity.

A heat up water to make steam

B wave movement

C tidal movement

D generator – a big coil of wire turns in a magnetic field

E solar voltaic cells

F releases carbon dioxide gas

G wind movement

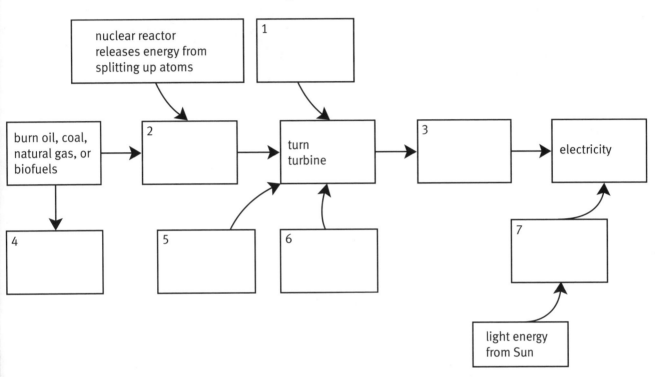

2 The data in the table are about electricity generated from different energy sources.

Use the data to write one argument that supports each person's opinion.

	Nuclear	Wind	Coal
Approximate efficiency	35%	59% of wind's energy can be extracted by blades	35%
Environmental impact	produce radioactive waste	some people think they look unattractive and that they are too noisy	contribute to acid rain
Cost per unit of electricity (pence)	3.0–4.0	3.0–4.0	3.0–3.5
Tonnes of carbon dioxide made for one terajoule of electricity	30	10	260

P 3

Opinions:

I think we should build more nuclear power stations.

Ben

Wind power is the answer!

Scarlett

Anything but nuclear!

Indi

It's better if we stick to generating electricity with coal.

Abdul

Arguments:

Ben: _____

_____

Scarlett: _____

_____

Indi: _____

_____

Abdul: _____

_____

3 Draw arrows to link each label to one or both people.

A This person has breathed in a radioactive chemical. He is contaminated.

B A radioactive source is irradiating this person.

C Ionizing radiation will stop hitting body cells
 • either when the radioactivity of the source decreases to zero
 • or when the source is removed from body

D Big doses of ionizing radiation kill cells.

E Smaller doses of ionizing radiation can damage cells.

F Ionizing radiation stops hitting body cells when he moves away from the source.

radioactive source.

radioactive source inside person's body.

P3.1.1–3 What energy sources do we use?

The demand for energy is increasing because:

- the world's population is increasing
- people travel further and have more possessions.

The increasing energy demand causes concerns about:

- the availability of energy sources
- the environmental impacts of using energy sources.

Primary energy sources exist naturally. They include fossil fuels (coal, oil, and gas), nuclear fuels, biofuels, wind, waves, and radiation from the Sun.

Electricity is a **secondary energy source**. It is generated from a primary source.

P3.1.5–8 How do we calculate electricity use?

When an electric current passes through a device, energy is transferred from the power supply to the device and the environment.

The power of a device or power station is the amount of energy it transfers each second,
or the rate at which it transfers energy. Different devices have different power ratings.

You can use this equation to calculate the power of a device:

$$\underset{\text{(watts, W)}}{\textbf{power}} \quad = \quad \underset{\text{(volts, V)}}{\textbf{voltage}} \quad \times \quad \underset{\text{(amps, A)}}{\textbf{current}}$$

Use this equation to calculate the energy transferred by a device:

$$\underset{\substack{\text{(joules, J)}\\\text{(kilowatt-hours, kWh)}}}{\textbf{energy transferred}} \quad = \quad \underset{\substack{\text{(watts, W)}\\\text{(kilowatts, kW)}}}{\textbf{power}} \quad \times \quad \underset{\substack{\text{(seconds, s)}\\\text{(hours, h)}}}{\textbf{time}}$$

A joule is a tiny amount of energy, so home electricity meters measure energy transfer in **kilowatt-hours**. One kilowatt-hour is the energy transferred by a 1 kW appliance in 1 hour.

$$3\,600\,000 \text{ J} = 1 \text{ kWh} = 1 \textbf{ unit}$$

You can calculate the cost of energy supplied by electricity like this:

$$\textbf{cost = power} \times \textbf{time} \times \textbf{cost per kilowatt-hour}$$

Worked example

Jason spends half an hour ironing shirts with a 3 kW iron. One unit of electricity costs 10p.

$$\text{cost} = 3 \text{ kW} \times 0.5 \text{ h} \times 10\text{p/kWh} = 15\text{p}$$

P 3

P3.1.11,14, P3.3.1 Can we cut energy use?

Individuals use energy for heating, transport, and using electrical devices. Energy is used to produce food, drink, and the other things we buy.

Public services and companies use energy for activities like building houses, running supermarkets, and powering computer servers. Individuals and workplaces can cut energy use by:
- switching off electrical devices
- using devices that are energy efficient.

Nationally, we could cut energy use by improving public transport, or by generating electricity more efficiently.

P3.1.12–13 What is efficiency?

For an electrical device or a power station:

$$\text{efficiency} = \frac{\textbf{energy usefully transferred}}{\textbf{total energy supplied}} \times \textbf{100\%}$$

Worked example

A 150 W flat screen TV transfers 50 J of energy as light and sound each second.

In one second, the total energy supplied is 150 J.

So the efficiency of the TV is $\frac{50}{150} \times 100\% = 33\%$

The Sankey diagram shows how energy is transferred by the TV. The total width of arrows on a Sankey diagram stays the same, because energy is **conserved** – it cannot be created or destroyed.

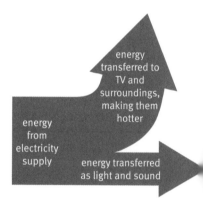

energy transferred to TV and surroundings, making them hotter

energy from electricity supply

energy transferred as light and sound

P3.2.1–6 How is electricity generated?

Electricity is convenient. It can be used in many ways, and transmitted long distances.

Generators make electricity by **electromagnetic induction**. In a generator, a magnet spins near a coil of wire. This induces a voltage across the ends of the coil. If the coil is part of a circuit, the induced voltage makes a current flow.

While the magnet is being removed from the coil, there is again a small current, but now in the opposite direction.

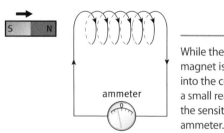

ammeter

While the bar magnet is moving into the coil, there is a small reading on the sensitive ammeter.

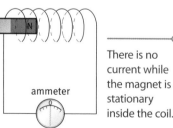

ammeter

There is no current while the magnet is stationary inside the coil.

ammeter

In **thermal power stations**, steam keeps the coil spinning. The steam comes from heating water. Primary sources (fossil fuels, nuclear power, or biofuels) supply the heat.

The more primary fuel supplied each second, the greater the current produced.

The diagram shows how thermal power stations generate electricity.

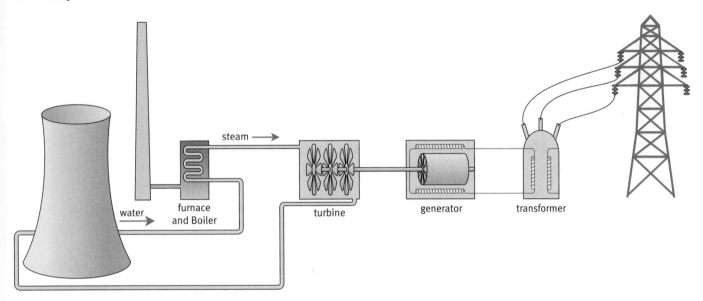

Electrical generation is never 100% efficient. The Sankey diagrams show the efficiency of coal-fired and gas-fired power stations.

P3.2.7–10 What happens in nuclear power stations?

In nuclear reactors, uranium atoms split up. This releases heat. The heat boils water to make steam. The steam turns a turbine connected to a generator, as in a thermal power station.

Nuclear fuels are **radioactive**. They make **radioactive waste**. Radioactive waste emits **ionising radiation**, which damages living cells. This damage can lead to cancer or cell death.

If you are exposed to ionising radiation, you have been **irradiated**. Radioactive **contamination** happens when radioactive material lands on or in a person or object. The person or object becomes radioactive, which may lead to long-term irradiation.

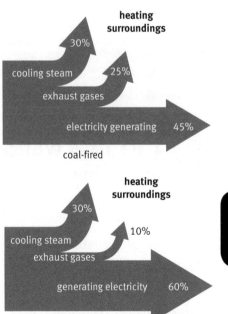

Sankey diagrams show what happens to all the energy. Less energy is wasted in a gas-fired power station.

P3.2.11 How do renewable sources generate electricity?

Many renewable energy sources turn turbines directly.
* Moving air turns **wind** turbines.
* **Wave** movements turn wave turbines.
* Falling **water** turns turbines in **hydroelectric** power stations.

P 3

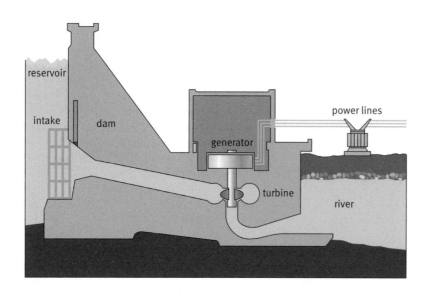

Water from the reservoir turns turbines, which turn the generator.

P3.2.12–13 How is electricity distributed?

The **National Grid** distributes electricity all over Britain. It uses **transformers** to change the voltage. Transmitting at high voltage (so that the current is small) minimises the energy lost as heat.

Electricity is supplied to homes at 230 volts in the UK.

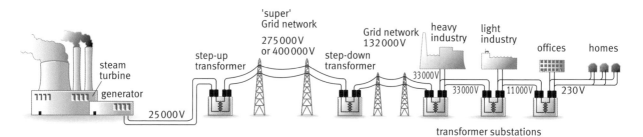

P3.1.4, P3.3.2–5 Which energy sources should we choose?

The choice of energy sources depends on factors including environmental impact, economics, waste, and CO_2 emissions.

H To be sure of a reliable electricity supply, a country needs a mix of energy sources.

When making decisions about generating electricity, energy planners need to consider:
- the expected power output of a power station
- the expected lifetime of a power station.

Exam tip

You might well be asked for advantages and disadvantages of different energy sources in the exam. Make sure you revise them carefully!

Use extra paper to answer these questions if you need to.

1 Tick the boxes to show which energy sources are renewable.

 a coal ☐

 b biofuels ☐

 c waves ☐

 d wind ☐

 e geothermal ☐

 f solar ☐

2 Draw lines to match each quantity to the correct units. Some quantities have more than one unit.

Quantity
voltage
energy
current
time
power

Unit
kilowatt-hour
joule
amp
watt
second
hour
volt

3 Put ticks in the boxes to show which energy sources each statement applies to.

	Biofuels	Gas	Solar
It is a primary energy source.			
When electricity is generated from it, CO_2 is produced.			
The generation of electricity from this source is weather dependent.			
When electricity is generated from it, no waste is produced.			

4 The statements below describe the energy flow in a nuclear power station. Write the letters of the steps in the correct order.

 A Uranium atoms in the solid fuel split up.

 B The hot fuel boils water.

 C A magnet turns in a coil of wire.

 D Steam drives turbines.

 E An electric current flows.

 F This releases energy and heats the fuel.

 G This induces a voltage across the ends of the coil.

5 Calculate the missing numbers in the table. One kilowatt (kW) is 1000 watts (W).

Device	Power rating (W)	Power rating (kW)	Time it is on for	Energy transferred (kWh)
computer	250	0.250	2 h	
kettle	1800	1.800	3 min	
toaster			5 min	0.10
phone charger			2 h	0.04

6 List three ways in which an individual can reduce the amount of energy they use.

7 List three ways in which a government can reduce the amount of energy used in its country.

8 One unit (kWh) of electricity costs 10p. Calculate the cost of using the following electrical items:

 a a 1.9 kW washing machine for 1.25 hours

 b a 0.5 kW surround sound system for 2 hours.

9 Work out the missing numbers in the Sankey diagrams.

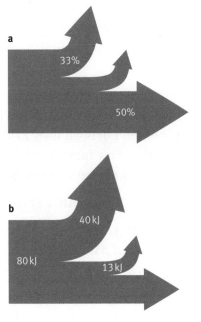

a

33%

50%

b

40 kJ

80 kJ

13 kJ

10 Explain why, in a Sankey diagram, the total width of the arrows must not change.

Ⓗ 11 Write a definition for the **power** of an appliance or device. Include the word *rate* in your definition.

12 Explain why a country needs a mix of energy sources.

P3

1 Read the article.

> **Portugal – leading the way in renewables**
>
> Between 2005 and 2010, the percentage of electricity generated from renewables in Portugal increased from 17% to 45%. This compares with 7% for the UK in 2010.
>
> In 2011, Portugal switched on mainland Europe's biggest wind farm. Portugal is soon to finish building the world's biggest solar power plant. The country is the first to generate electricity from wave power. Portugal also generates much electricity in hydroelectric power stations.

a Portugal's biggest wind farm has 120 turbines.
Each can supply 2 MW of electricity.

    i Calculate the electrical power that can be supplied by all 120 turbines of the wind farm.

Answer = _____ MW [2]

    ii Calculate the electrical energy supplied by the wind farm in 24 hours, if it is windy.

Answer = _____ MWh [2]

b The energy supplied by Portugal's biggest hydroelectric power station in one day is 15 120 000 kWh.
An average person in Portugal uses 13 kWh of electricity in one day. Calculate how many people the hydroelectric power station can supply with electricity for a day.

Answer = _____ people [2]

c Portugal's new solar power plant will have 2520 solar panels, each the size of a house. They are tilted.

    i During one 24-hour period, each solar panel will turn around through an angle greater than 200°. Suggest why.

_____ [1]

    ii The total energy supplied to a solar panel in one second is 120 000 J.
The useful energy transferred is 18 000 J.
Calculate the efficiency of a solar panel.

Answer = _____ % [2]

d The table gives the approximate efficiency for three methods of generating electricity.

Method of generating electricity	Efficiency
geothermal	16%
wind	59% of wind's energy extracted by blades
hydroelectric	90%

Suggest why Portugal uses wind power to generate electricity, as well as hydroelectric power stations, even though the efficiency for wind power is lower.

_____ [1]

e In 2008, Portugal opened the world's first wave farm. It is 5 km off the coast of Portugal. It converts energy in waves to electrical energy.

  i Before it was built, many people supported the idea of having a wave farm. Suggest why.

  _____ [1]

  ii Some people were against the wave farm. Suggest why.

  _____ [1]

Total [12]

2 A government wants to increase the amount of biofuels used to fuel cars, and decrease the amount of petrol and diesel.

Evaluate the benefits and problems of replacing fossil fuels with biofuels.

The quality of written communication will be assessed in your answer to this question.
Write your answer on separate paper or in your exercise book.

Total [6]

3 In 2008, a power station in Poland announced plans to expand.

The power station burns coal from its own mine, which is next to the power station.
The power station produces more carbon dioxide than any other power station in Europe.

P
3

a Use the words below to label the diagram of a coal-fired power station.
Write one word in each box.

furnace   steam   generator   transformer

turbine   water

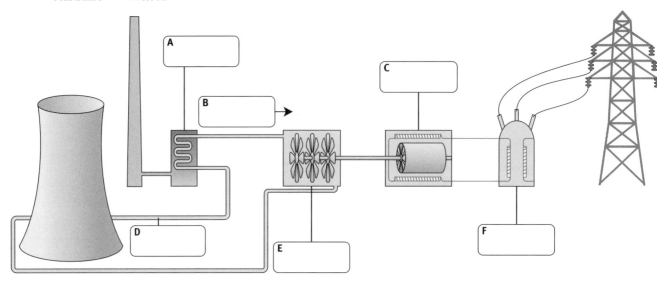

[3]

b The Sankey diagram below shows what happens to the energy in a coal-fired power station.

Calculate the percentage of energy that is carried away by exhaust gases.

Answer = _____ %   [1]

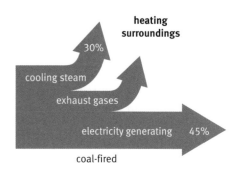

c Some people think the power station should not expand.
Suggest one reason for this.

_____

_____ [1]

d Some people think the power station should be replaced by a nuclear power station.
Give reasons for and against this idea.

_____

_____

_____

_____

_____ [3]

Total [8]

Ideas about science

Data: their importance and limitations

1

It says here that the concentration of nitrogen dioxide in the air in London is more than it is anywhere else in Britain. I don't believe it. In my **opinion,** the idea's a load of rubbish!

2

It's not just an idea. My newspaper has lots of **data to justify the statement.** Scientists have measured the nitrogen dioxide concentration in many places.

3

OK. But how do we know their data are **any good**? Do we know **how close to the true value** their measurements are?

4

Good question. Maybe the measuring instruments were faulty. And even if all the scientists used the same instrument, they could have used it in different ways and got different results. And, of course, the concentration of nitrogen dioxide in any one place changes all the time!

5

So you're saying the data are not accurate?

6

No. In each place, the scientists took **many measurements**.

7

Why did they bother?

8

*If they just made one measurement, they could not have been sure it was accurate. So they made many measurements. Then they calculated the mean. The **mean is a good estimate of the true value.***

9

Here's another problem: some of the data could be very different from the true value. May be something odd happenend while they were taking measurements, or someone made a mistake.

10

*Exactly. One or two of the readings might have been very different from most of the others – they're called **outliers**.*

11

Where possible, scientists check an outlier to see if it is correct or not. If it is wrong, scientists discard it before calculating the mean.

12

If scientists cannot check an outlier, but have good reason to think it is inaccurate, they may discard it. But if there is no reason to discard an outlier, they treat it as data.

1

Dad, this scientific paper says that traffic exhaust is the single most serious preventable cause of heart attacks. Aren't the particulates in diesel exhaust particularly bad? I don't think you should get a diesel car.

2

Don't worry. We're buying the new Cheetah. The data from the makers show that its particulate emissions are the lowest of all diesel cars.

3

Yeah right. It could be a one-off. How do you know the data are **repeatable**?

Their engineers did the test many times in the same conditions. They got similar results each time. So the data are **repeatable**.

4

But are the measurements **reproducible**? Would they be the same if different engineers did the tests, or they used different methods?

Hmm. I'm not sure, son.

5

Anyway, is the Cheetah better than our old Tiger? Is there a real difference in the amounts of particulates they emit?

6

I'd need to compare sets of data from both cars. If their **means are different and their ranges do not overlap**, I'd be confident there was a real difference.

Data: their importance and limitations

1 Solve the clues to fill in the grid opposite.
You will need the data in the table to help you fill in some of the words.

Metal	Melting point (°C)	Density (g/cm³)
gold	1063	19.3
lead	327	11.3
iron	1535	7.9
silver	961	10.5
cadmium	321	8.6
zinc	420	7.1

1 Scientists create explanations to account for . . .

2 A student measured the melting point of lead six times.
The highest value she obtained was 329 °C, and the lowest
value was 324 °C. So the . . . of the readings was 324–329 °C.

3 A measurement that lies well outside the range of the
others in a set of repeats is called an . . .

4 Data that are . . . do not vary much when you repeat the
measurements under the same conditions.

5 Of the metals in the table, iron has the highest . . .

6 Faulty measuring equipment leads to . . . data.

7 The best estimate of the value of a quantity is the . . . of
several repeat measurements.

8 Iron has a . . . density than zinc.

9 The mean of several repeat measurements is the best
estimate of the . . . value of a quantity.

10 To get the best estimate of the true value of a quantity,
take several . . . measurements and calculate the mean.

11 Of the metals in the table, zinc has the . . . density.

12 All the metals in the table are . . . at room temperature.

13 Scientists use data rather than . . . to justify an
explanation.

Ⓗ 14 If the mean of a set of readings for one sample is within
the range of a set of readings for another sample, there
is . . . real difference between the true values of the two
samples.

15 A student measured the melting point of a metal in the
table several times. She calculated that the mean of her
measurements was 959 °C. She concluded that the metal
was probably . . .

1 d
2 a
3 t
4 a
5 l
6 i
7 m
8 i
9 t
10 a
11 t
12 i
13 o
14 n
15 s

2 The ideal air temperature of a baby's bedroom is 18 °C. A father is worried that the room is too cold, so he hangs a mercury thermometer on the wall between the curtain and the window. He uses the thermometer to measure the temperature, and gets a reading of 15 °C.

Give three reasons why the measurement may not give you the correct value for the air temperature in the room.

____

____

____

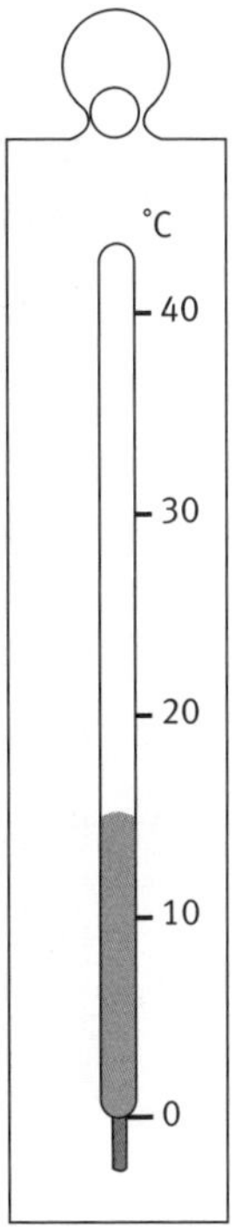
°C
40
30
20
10
0

3 Each table is designed to collect a set of data about an air pollutant, sulfur dioxide.

Give the letter or letters of the best table or tables in which to collect data to compare:

a the concentrations of a pollutant in the four seasons of the year

_____

b the concentrations of a pollutant on weekdays and at the weekend _____

c the concentrations of a pollutant at different times of day

_____

d the concentrations of a pollutant in two different cities _____

A

Place: Prague			
Date	Day	Time	Concentration of sulfur dioxide (µg/m³)
3 Jan	Mon	11.00	
6 April	Wed	11.00	
7 July	Thu	11.00	
7 Oct	Fri	11.00	

B

Place: Paris			
Date	Day	Time	Concentration of sulfur dioxide (µg/m³)
3 Jan	Mon	11.00	
5 Jan	Wed	11.00	
6 Jan	Thu	11.00	
9 Jan	Sun	11.00	

C

Place: Brussels			
Date	Day	Time	Concentration of sulfur dioxide (µg/m³)
3 Jan	Mon	11.00	
6 April	Wed	12.00	
7 July	Thu	10.00	
2 Oct	Sun	11.00	

D

Place: Leipzig			
Date	Day	Time	Concentration of sulfur dioxide (µg/m³)
7 July	Thu	08.00	
7 July	Thu	12.00	
7 July	Thu	17.00	
7 July	Thu	22.00	

Data: their importance and limitations

1 Scientists measured the salt content of hamburgers from two restaurants.

They tested six hamburgers from each restaurant.

Their results are in the table.

Sample	\multicolumn{6}{c}{Salt content (g)}	Range	Mean
	1	2	3	4	5	6	Range	Mean
Restaurant A	0.9	1.1	1.0	1.3	0.5	1.2	0.5–1.3	1.0
Restaurant B	1.6	1.4	1.2	1.4	1.3	1.5		

a **i** Identify the outlier in the data from restaurant A.

Outlier is sample _____. [1]

ii The scientists decided to include the outlier in the range and mean for restaurant A. Suggest why.

_____ [1]

b Work out the range and the mean for the samples from restaurant B.

Range = _____ to _____ g

Mean = _____ g [2]

c The scientists conclude that there is a **real difference** between the salt content of the hamburgers from the two restaurants.

Explain how the data in the table and your answer to part **b** show this.

_____

_____ [1]

d A different group of scientists measured the salt content of hamburgers from restaurant B.

Their mean value was the same as that of the scientists whose results are in the table above.

What does this show?

Put a tick in **one** box next to the best answer below.

The data for restaurant B are repeatable. ☐

The two sets of data have the same range. ☐

The data for restaurant B are reproducible. ☐

The two sets of data are identical. ☐ [1]

Total [6]

2 Ten students measured the concentration of sulfur dioxide in the air in central Manchester at the same time. Here are the data they collected.

Student	L	M	N	O	P	Q	R	S	T	U
Concentration of sulfur dioxide (μg/m³)	25	20	22	26	27	28	11	31	23	20

a Plot the data on the graph axis below.
One point has been plotted for you.

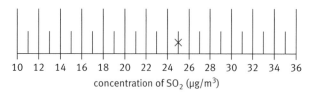

concentration of SO₂ (μg/m³)   **[2]**

b i On your graph, circle the outlier for this set of data.

[1]

ii Suggest one possible reason for this measurement being so different from the others.

_____ **[1]**

c i Ten students measured the concentration of sulfur dioxide in the air in central Birmingham at the same time. Here are the data they collected.

Student	A	B	C	D	E	F	G	H	I	J
Concentration of sulfur dioxide (μg/m³)	25	27	30	34	22	29	28	26	28	21

Calculate the mean concentration of sulfur dioxide in the air in Birmingham.

Mean = _____ μg/m³   **[1]**

ii Work out the range of the sulfur dioxide concentration measurements.

Range = _____ to _____ μg/m³   **[1]**

Total [6]

3 A group of students in the Czech Republic studied data and devised this scientific explanation:

> There is a correlation between being exposed to air pollution and the percentage of sperm with damaged DNA.

1

a The students collected data on one pollutant, sulfur dioxide.

They measured its concentration at the same place every day for six months.
Their measurements were different every day.

Why were the measurements different every day?
Put ticks in the boxes next to three possible reasons

Wind direction varied. ☐

A nearby coal-fired power station was running on some days, but not on others. ☐

One student used the measuring instrument incorrectly. ☐

A nearly nuclear power station was running on some days, but not on others. ☐ [1]

b Suggest what other data the students needed to collect to provide evidence for the explanation in the box.

_____

_____ [1]

Total [2]

4 Engineers from two factories tested the carbon dioxide emissions of two different cars of the same make and model.

Their data are in the table.

	Carbon dioxide emissions (g/km)					
Sample	1	2	3	4	5	6
Car A	153	158	159	163	157	158
Car B	156	164	160	163	160	157

Use the data to decide whether or not there is a real difference between the carbon dioxide emissions of the two cars.

Write down your decision.

Use data from the table to explain how and why you came to this decision.

The quality of written communication will be assessed in your answer to this question.

Write your answer on separate paper or in your exercise book.

Total [6]

5 A scientist reads in a journal that shellfish cannot make their shells in seawater below a certain pH.

He knows that when carbon dioxide dissolves in seawater, the pH of the seawater gets lower.

He knows that the concentration of atmospheric carbon dioxide (CO_2) is increasing.

The scientist wants to predict how the changing concentration of atmospheric CO_2 will affect shellfish.

a The scientist studies data on past and present concentrations of atmospheric CO_2. He thinks about the data and predicts future concentrations of atmospheric CO_2.

Which data set is most useful in predicting future concentrations of atmospheric CO_2?

Tick **one** box.

the concentrations of atmospheric CO_2 in 1900 and now ☐

the concentrations of atmospheric CO_2 in 1990, 2000, and now ☐

the amounts of CO_2 released to the atmosphere from the UK in 1990, 2000, and now ☐

the amounts of CO_2 released to the atmosphere from the UK in 1900 and now ☐

[1]

b The scientist assumes that as atmospheric CO_2 concentrations increase, so the concentration of CO_2 that dissolves in seawater will increase.

Suggest what data the scientist can collect to support his assumption.

_____

_____ [2]

c At the end of his work, the scientist makes this prediction:

'By 2050 the pH of sea water will be too low for shellfish to make shells.'

Suggest two reasons why a scientist who studies shellfish in 2050 might find that the shellfish can, in fact, make shells.

_____

_____ [2]

Total [5]

> **Exam tip**
>
> Read questions carefully. If you are asked for two reasons, make sure you give two reasons, not just one.

Cause–effect explanations

China plans to reduce the power station emissions that cause acid rain. It says that acid rain damages its trees, crops, and buildings.

OK. So one of the **outcomes** is that trees are damaged. But surely acid rain is not the only **factor** that affects the amount of damage?

True. There are many other possible factors. Maybe diseases, pests, or even climate change damage China's trees. But there's lots of scientific evidence that acid rain is an important factor.

So changing this factor . . . reducing the amount of acid rain . . . could change the outcome? Fewer trees would be damaged?

Let's hope so!

My company is planning to manufacture bungee-jumping ropes. We need to investigate which material to use. To start with, I want to know which material is strongest.

OK. So you've got a machine that measures the force needed to break ropes made from the different materials?

Yes. And we've got these samples of materials. We'll just put them into the machine.

There'd be a few **design flaws** if you did that! You need to think carefully about what **factors to control** to make the test fair.

Like all the samples being the same thickness?

Yes. And they must all be woven into ropes in exactly the same way.
If you don't control all the factors that might affect the outcome – except the one you're investigating – then your results are meaningless. You will know almost nothing about the relationship between the factor you're investigating and the outcome.

1

Look at this! It says that drinking alcohol gives you mouth cancer! I'm going to lose my tongue and lips – yuk! I'm never drinking again!

2

Not so fast! Read it carefully! It says that that alcohol is a **risk factor** for the disease. Smoking is another one.

3

Ah, it's like we were doing in science. Drinking alcohol is **a factor that increases the chance of the outcome** – getting mouth cancer. But it's not definite that I'll get it.

4

Of course you won't get it. My auntie drank loads. She never got mouth cancer.

5

That's just one case. It tells you almost nothing. You need a much bigger sample to provide convincing evidence for or against a correlation.

6

Correlation? What's that?

2

7

It's when *an outcome variable increases (or decreases) steadily as an input variable increases*. So as the amount of alcohol drunk by British people increases, so does the number of cases of mouth cancer. You can also say there's a correlation because drinking alcohol *increases a person's chance* of getting mouth cancer.

8

It's like this – as the number of hours of sunshine in Blackpool goes up, so does the number of cases of sunburn. That's a **correlation** between a **factor** (hours of sunshine) and an **outcome** (how many people get sunburnt).

9

Or this survey we did at primary school. We found that taller children are better at adding up than shorter children.

10

Exactly. They're both correlations. There's probably good evidence that an increase in the hours of sunshine **causes** the number of sunburnt people to increase.
But I doubt if it's like that for your survey. Increasing height is unlikely to cause an increase in children's ability to add up. Probably, they're both caused by some other factor – maybe increasing age.

1

'Cold noses give you colds,' say Cardiff scientists. Their evidence comes from a simple experiment – getting 90 volunteers to sit with their feet in icy cold water for 20 minutes. Five days later, 29% of them had colds. Only 9% of a control group – who dangled their feet in empty bowls – became poorly.

2

What do you think? Does the factor of having a cold nose increase your chance of the outcome – getting a cold?

Hmm. Good question. They're **comparing two samples**, which is good. I'd like to know how well the **samples matched**.

3

You mean it would be a poorly designed study if the average age of one group were much older than that of the people in the other group?

Exactly. That's a good example. The **sample size** is important too – the bigger the sample, the more confident I'd be in the conclusions.

4

But how can they say 'cold noses give you colds'? The study is all about feet?

The scientists must have thought of a sensible **mechanism to link the factor to the outcome**. If they didn't they wouldn't say that one thing caused the other, even though there's a correlation. Let's read on . . .

5

Here we are. The scientists say that when you are cold, you get a cold nose. The blood vessels in your nose get smaller. So fewer white blood cells – the ones that fight infection – get to where they're needed (in your nose!).

Clever! So there's good **reason to accept the causal link** that they claim.

Cause–effect explanations

1 Circle the letters of the graphs that show a correlation between
a factor and an outcome.

A

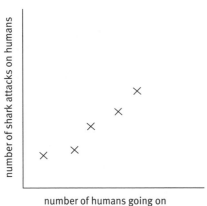

B

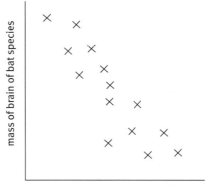

C

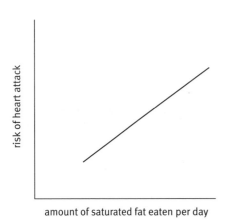

D

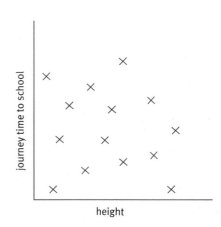

E

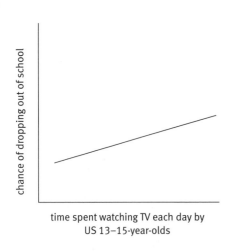

F

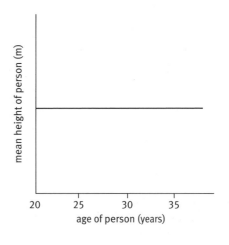

2 Solve the anagrams.
Match each anagram answer to a clue.

Clues	Anagrams
A To investigate whether a factor affects an outcome, we compare samples. The _____ the samples, the more confident we can be in the conclusions.	**1** for cats
B If an outcome variable increases as an input variable increases, there is a _____ between the variables.	**2** cute moo
C Eating food high in saturated fats increases your _____ of having a heart attack.	**3** erotic lorna
D When investigating the relationship between a factor and an outcome, it is vital to _____ all the factors that might affect the outcome.	**4** corn lot
E Scientists usually only believe that a factor causes an outcome if there is a plausible _____ that links the factor to the outcome.	**5** us aces
F When comparing samples, the samples must be either _____ or _____.	**6** achenc
G Many factors can affect an _____.	**7** mad tech
H _____ are input variables that may affect an outcome.	**8** erglar
I A correlation between a factor and an outcome does not necessarily mean that one _____ the other.	**9** can she mim
	10 arm nod

Cause–effect explanations

1 A shampoo company claimed:

> In only 10 days, our anti-break shampoo gives up to 95% less hair breakage than other shampoos.

Scientists at the company tested 10 samples of hair, three times each.

2

a Identify the factor (input variable) and the outcome (outcome variable) in the investigation.

Factor: _____

Outcome: _____ [1]

b A school student decided to investigate the company's claims.
He used this apparatus to test hair strength.

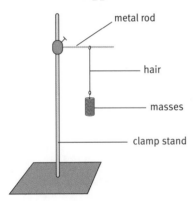

i Give two factors the student must control.

_____

_____ [2]

ii Explain why the student must control these factors.

_____ [1]

c The student found that a greater weight was needed to break hair that had been washed with anti-break shampoo.

Explain why this correlation does not necessarily mean that the shampoo makes hair stronger. [1]

_____

_____

_____

Total [5]

2 In December 2005, there was a huge fire at an oil depot in southern England. Some of the chemicals in the smoke were:

> **carbon monoxide, sulfur dioxide, nitrogen dioxide, solid carbon**

a Tick one box next to each statement to show whether the statement is an outcome or a factor that may affect one or more of the outcomes. There are three factors and three outcomes. One has been done for you.

Statement		Outcome	Factor
A	Smoke from the fire rose 3000 m above the ground.		
B	The atmospheric concentration of sulfur dioxide 3000 m over southern England increased.		
C	The atmospheric concentration of nitrogen dioxide near the ground over southern England changed very little.		
D	The smoke was trapped 3000 m above the ground.		✔
E	The atmospheric concentration of carbon monoxide over northern England did not change.		
F	Wind carried the smoke south.		

[2]

b Imagine factor D had been different, and the smoke had not been trapped high above the ground.

In the table below, give the letters of the **two** outcomes that might have been affected.

Then suggest **how** each of these outcomes might have been affected.

Outcome	How the outcome might have been affected

[2]

c Nitrogen dioxide gas is the only gas produced by the fire that increases the risk of asthma attacks.

Draw straight lines to match each comment with one conclusion.

Comment
1 When the concentration of carbon monoxide increases, there is no change in the number of asthma attacks.
2 More asthma sufferers had asthma attacks in the week after the fire than in a normal week. But not every asthma sufferer had an attack.
3 When the concentration of nitrogen dioxide gas in the air increases, more asthma sufferers have asthma attacks.
4 I know three people who had asthma attacks after the fire.

Conclusion
A There is a correlation between this factor and this outcome.
B These cases do not provide evidence for or against a correlation between the factor and the outcome.
C There is no correlation between this factor and this outcome.
D The factor increased the chance of the outcome but did not always lead to it.

[3]

Total [7]

Going for the highest grades

3 Read the article in the box.
Then answer the question below it.

> In 2004, Ireland banned smoking in all workplaces, including pubs.
>
> The next year, scientists studied air quality and staff health in a sample of 40 Irish pubs.
>
> The scientists found that, since 2004, pub workers had had fewer symptoms of smoke irritation, such as watery eyes. Pub workers' breathing difficulties had decreased by 70%. The scientists also found that, since 2004, the mean concentration of carbon monoxide in pub workers' exhaled breath had decreased by 40%.

Use examples from the article to help you explain ideas about correlation and cause.

The quality of written communication will be assessed in your answer to this question.

Write your answer on separate paper or in your exercise book.

Total [6]

4 The concentration of ozone in the upper atmosphere has decreased since 1960.

Ozone protects humans from the harmful effects of the Sun's ultraviolet radiation, like getting eye cataracts.

American scientists wanted to know if the 'thinning' ozone layer would lead to more people getting eye cataracts. They studied 2500 people.

Their results showed that **if the concentration of ozone decreases by 20%, the number of people with cataracts is likely to increase by 7%.**

a Tick the boxes next to the three statements that could be true.

The smaller the concentration of ozone in the upper atmosphere, the greater your chance of getting a cataract. ☐

There is a correlation between the concentration of ozone in the upper atmosphere and the number of people with cataracts. ☐

Wearing sunglasses that protect against ultraviolet radiation may reduce your chance of getting a cataract. ☐

If the concentration of ozone in the upper atmosphere increases, the number of people with cataracts is likely to increase. ☐ [1]

b A British scientist wants to find out if there is a correlation between the amount of exposure to the Sun's ultraviolet radiation and the risk of getting a cataract.

She decides to compare two groups of people. All the people in one sample have cataracts; all those in the other sample do not have cataracts.

i Draw a ring around the sample size that will give the most reliable conclusion.

10   100   1000
as large as practically possible [1]

ii The scientist makes sure that the two samples are matched for age.

Suggest two other factors that she must match.

_____

_____ [2]

Total [4]

> **Exam tip**
>
> Remember – just because there is a correlation between a factor and an outcome, it does not mean that the factor caused the outcome.

Developing scientific explanations

1 It's 2010. A team of geologists are on a boat, north of Scotland. They send sound waves more than 2 km below the seafloor, and analyse the echoes that come back up to the boat.

> *These data are amazing. I've never seen anything like it. In some places, the bottom of this mudstone layer is 1 km below the seafloor. But in other places, the mudstone goes down much deeper.*

> *We're certainly not looking at boring layers of mud and sand. Let's map the data. Then maybe we can come up with an explanation.*

2 One year later, at a scientific conference.

> *I mapped the data. The shape of the rock under the mudstone, 2 km below the seafloor, looks like the surface of land, with hills, valleys, and rivers. We **thought creatively** about the data, and came up with an **hypothesis – an explanation that might account for the data**.*

3

> *Here's our hypothesis: 56 million years ago, seafloor rock was forced upwards, above the surface of the sea. For two million years, wind and water shaped the landscape. Then the land sank down again, beneath the sea. Here, it was covered with sediment, which formed new layers of rock that buried the landscape.*
>
> *We think the landscape rock was forced up and then down by hot mantle material moving beneath the seafloor tectonic plate.*

4

> *From our hypothesis, we made a **prediction**. There are fossils of land plants in the rock that was once land. There are fossils of sea animals in the layers of rock above and below the rock that was once land.*

5

> *An oil company drilled through the rock, and gave us samples. Our prediction was correct. This made us **more confident in our explanation**. Of course, we **cannot prove** our explanation is correct.*

1 It's 1924. Two scientists are reporting their latest fossil find.

Before we found the skull, we were confident in the explanation that human ancestors developed big brains before they walked upright. We predicted that any fossils we found would support this explanation.

This is it. A fossilised skull from the first human species: australopithecine.

2

But this fossil certainly doesn't! We've observed it carefully, and can see that its owner had a small brain and walked upright.

So our **observations of this new find disagree with our prediction**. We're now much **less confident in the explanation** that humans had big brains before they walked upright.

Developing scientific explanations

1 The statements below describe how a group of scientists tested a hypothesis about the evolution of banded snails between 2009 and 2011. Banded snails have a variety of different shell colours.

Write the letter of each statement in a box on the flow chart. There is one letter for each box.

A Snails have evolved since the 1970s because the climate has got hotter, and a light-coloured shell may protect a snail from overheating.

B In 2009 and 2010, more than 6000 people in 15 countries counted banded snails of different shell colours. A scientist found records of snail shell colours from the 1970s.

C Between 1970 and 2010 there was an increase in the percentage of snails with one dark spiral band around their shells. The percentage of snails with light-coloured shells had not changed.

D A scientist observed banded snails with different shell colours. The percentage of snails of each shell colour seemed to have changed since the 1970s.

E The percentage of snails with light-coloured shells will be greater in 2010 than in 1970.

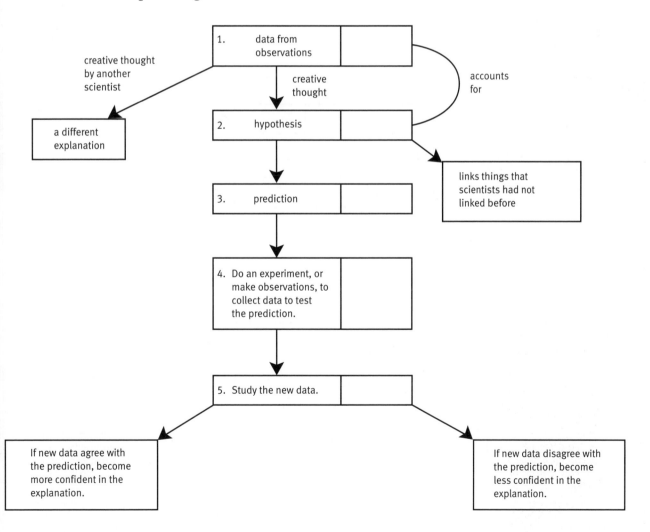

3

2 The statements below describe how scientists developed an explanation about the antibacterial substances in crocodile blood.

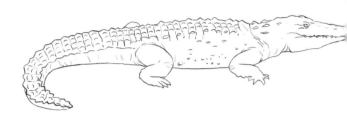

Write the letter of each statement in a box on the flow chart.
There is one letter for each box.
One letter has already been filled in.

A A scientist noticed that serious crocodile injuries heal quickly without getting infected.

B Crocodile blood will destroy microorganisms such as *E. coli*.

C The areas around the crocodile blood-soaked discs had no *E. coli* bacteria.

D The scientist soaked paper discs in crocodile blood extract. He placed these on agar plates with *E. coli* bacteria.

E Crocodile blood contains substances that destroy bacteria.

F After an injury, crocodiles wallow in mud that has antibacterial properties.

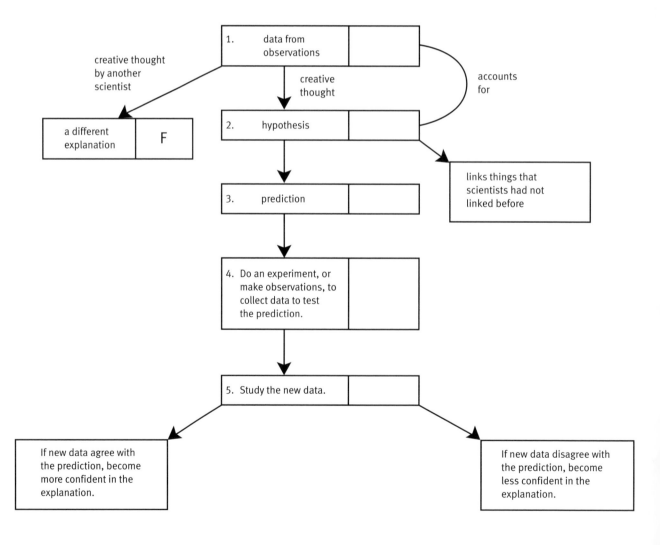

Developing scientific explanations

1 In Kenya, elephants sometimes go onto farmland and ruin maize crops. Some farmers kill these elephants.

Scientists wanted to explain why elephants go onto farmland. They could then predict when elephants were likely to go onto farmland.
The scientists could then tell farmers when to make the most effort to guard their crops from elephants.

The scientists studied seven elephants.

They found out where the elephants went and what they ate.

The statements opposite describe the scientists' work.

A The scientists thought that elephants might go onto farmland in the dry season only.	
B Satellite tracking showed that six elephants spent all their time in the lowlands.	
C Tail hair analysis from one elephant showed that he ate grass from the lowlands in wet seasons and maize from farmland in dry seasons.	
D In the dry season, there is not enough grass for elephants to eat. Some elephants get the food they need from shrubs and trees. But if there are not enough trees and shrubs, elephants take maize from farmland to eat.	
E Satellite tracking showed that one elephant spent the wet season in the lowlands and the dry season in a forest near farmland.	
F Tail hair analysis of six elephants showed that they ate trees and shrubs in the dry season. In the wet season they ate grass.	
G Fewer elephants will die if scientists find out when they are most likely to eat maize from farms.	

Some of these statements are **data** and one is a possible **explanation**.
Write a **D** next to the **four** statements that are data.
Write an **E** next to the **one** statement that is an explanation.

Total [5]

2 Read the article in the box.

It is about research reported in a scientific journal in 2011.

In a short visit to a small island, scientists identified more species of fanged frogs than on a bigger island nearby. They did not find any frogs from another group – the *Platymantis* group.

The scientists expected that every type of habitat on the small island would have its own species of fanged frogs. They went to many of these habitats, and identified the fanged frog species in each one. Many habitats had their own species of fanged frogs. The frog species had different sizes, different webbing on their feet, and raised their young differently.

The scientists thought about what they had seen. They suggested that the fanged frogs had evolved more on the small island because there was no competition from *Platymantis* frogs.

Explain how the description of the scientists' work in the box illustrates how scientific explanations develop.

The quality of written communication will be assessed in your answer to this question.

Write your answer on separate paper or in your exercise book.

Total [6]

3 Scientists wanted to find out whether smoking increases the risk of developing an eye disease called AMD. Most AMD sufferers are partially blind.

a The scientists recorded the following statements.

A The greater the number of years a person smokes, and the more they smoke each day, the greater their risk of developing AMD.	
B Eye doctors have noticed a build-up of waste substances near the retinas of smokers' eyes.	
C 12% of AMD sufferers smoked 20 cigarettes a day for more than 40 years.	
D Substances in cigarette smoke may cause damage to cells in the retina of the eye.	
E Eye doctors have observed that people with AMD have damaged retinas.	

Write the letter **D** next to the **three** statements that are data.

Write the letter **E** next to the **one** statement that is part of an explanation.

Write the letter **C** next to the **one** statement that is a conclusion drawn from data. [3]

b The scientists used their explanation to make this prediction:

> Passive smokers have a greater risk of developing AMD than people who are not exposed to cigarette smoke.

They collected the following data:
- Of 100 non-smokers with AMD, 72 were passive smokers.
- Of 100 non-smokers without AMD, 66 were passive smokers.

Put a tick in the **two** boxes next to the statements that are true.

The data increase confidence in the explanation. ☐

The data prove the explanation is correct. ☐

The data agree with the prediction. ☐

The data decrease confidence in the explanation. ☐ [2]

Total [5]

4 Nearly 2000 people who lived near Lake Nyos in Cameroon died in 1986.

a Scientists wanted to find out why the people died.
They collected these data:

A   Carbon dioxide is soluble in water.

B   If carbon dioxide takes the place of air, people die from lack of oxygen.

C   There is a volcano below Lake Nyos.

D   Carbon dioxide gas is denser than air.

E   Sometimes there are small Earth movements near Lake Nyos.

F   If you shake a saturated solution of a gas, some of the gas escapes from solution.

G   Carbon dioxide has no smell.

H   Magma contains dissolved carbon dioxide.

I   Carbon dioxide gas is invisible.

i   The scientists used their data to develop an explanation. The explanation is in six parts.

Next to each part of the explanation, write one or two letters to show which data each part of the explanation accounts for.

One has been done for you.

Do not write in the shaded boxes.

Part of explanation	Data that this part of the explanation accounts for	
1 Carbon dioxide gas bubbles into the bottom of Lake Nyos.	C	
2 Carbon dioxide dissolves to make a saturated solution.		
3 There was a small Earth movement. This released 80 million cubic metres of carbon dioxide gas from the lake.		
4 Carbon dioxide gas filled the valleys around the lake.		
5 No one detected the carbon dioxide gas, so no one ran away.		
6 1700 people died.		

[4]

ii   The explanation accounts for all the data.
Does this mean that the explanation must be correct?
Give a reason for your decision.

_____

_____ [1]

b Scientists predict that Lake Nyos will release carbon dioxide again in future. They expect more people to die. They do not know when this will happen.

Suggest one reason why the scientists cannot know when Lake Nyos will next release a large amount of carbon dioxide.

_____

_____ [1]

Total [6]

5 Scientists have studied earthquakes in areas near big, heavy structures made by humans. They created this explanation:

> Big and heavy structures cause changes in the forces in the ground. These changes may cause earthquakes.

a Study the data in the table.

A	In 1967 there was an earthquake near a huge dam in India. The dam had just been finished.
B	Since 2003, there have been two earthquakes near the world's tallest building, Taipei 101. Taipei 101 was finished in 2003. Before Taipei 101, there were very few earthquakes in the area.
C	In 1967 there was an earthquake under a US mountain. A company had just injected huge amounts of waste into the mountain.
D	The earthquakes under Taipei 101 happened 10 km underground. The building does not affect underground forces at this depth.
E	In 2001 there was an earthquake in the North Sea. Companies have taken many tonnes of oil and gas from the area.

i Give the letters of two pieces of data that the explanation accounts for.

_____ [2]

ii Give the letter of one piece of data that conflicts with the explanation.

_____ [1]

b Governments plan to store carbon dioxide in big
underground holes.

A scientist uses the explanation in the box to make this
prediction:

The scientist collects data from now until 2030. Imagine
the data shows that there had been five earthquakes near
carbon dioxide storage holes. Before the holes were made,
no earthquakes had been recorded in these areas.

Put ticks in the boxes that are true.

There will be more
earthquakes near carbon
dioxide storage holes than
there were in these areas
before the storage holes
were made.

The data would not prove the explanation
is correct. ☐

The data would agree with the prediction. ☐

The data would increase confidence in the
explanation. ☐

The data would decrease confidence in the
explanation. ☐ [2]

Total [5]

3

6 A scientist developed an explanation that doing exercise would decrease the effect that a high salt diet has on raising blood pressure.

The scientist predicted that:

The more active you are, the less your blood pressure will increase if you switch to a high salt diet.

The scientist collected data:

- She measured the blood pressure of 1000 volunteers who normally had a low salt diet.

- She asked the volunteers to eat a high salt diet for one week. She divided the volunteers into four groups. During this week, each volunteer did a different amount of exercise.

- At the end of the week, the scientist measured the volunteers' blood pressure again.

The results are in the table.

Group of volunteers	Change in blood pressure after eating a high salt diet for one week (mmHg)
least active	5.27
next-to-least active	5.07
next-to-most active	4.93
most active	3.88

Do you think other scientists should accept or reject the explanation?

Give reasons for your decision.

_____

_____

_____

_____

Total [4]

The scientific community

1

*New research shows that the brainier male bats are, the smaller their testicles. Scientists studied 334 bat species, and found a correlation between brain size and testicle size: species with small brains have big testicles. The testicles of one bat species account for 8% of male bats' body mass. The scientists reported their findings in a **peer-reviewed scientific journal**.*

2

So what do you think of that? That's equivalent to a man's testicles weighing about a stone! More than 6 kg! It can't be right, surely?

*Well, the research is about bats – the scientists don't claim to have found out anything about men! But other scientists must have **evaluated** the claim, because the radio report said that the scientific journal is peer-reviewed.*

3

Hmmm. It's a very new idea. I'm not sure I believe it.

*I know what you mean. Maybe the scientists were surprised at first. But they must have **replicated their own findings** before the journal agreed to publish them. So they were confident their claim was correct.*

4

*Has **anyone else reproduced** the research?*

Not as far as I know. The scientists reported exactly what they did. So other scientists could do a similar study. If the results were similar, there would be less reason to question the claim.

THE HISTORY PROGRAMME
Presenters' script

23/08/2012

Presenter 1 (Simon)

Welcome to *The History Programme*. This year, 2012, is the hundredth anniversary of Wegener's theory of continental drift. We all now recognise the importance of his ideas. But a century ago scientists laughed at him.

Presenter 2 (Janet)

Yes, that's right. Wegener explained that the east coast of South America was once joined to Africa's west coast. The two continents had been slowly moving apart ever since. Wegener had lots of data to support his explanation: the shapes, rock types, fossils, and mountain ranges of the two continents matched up closely.

Presenter 1

So why did other scientists disagree with Wegener?

Presenter 2

Well, of course you can't always deduce explanations from data. So it's quite reasonable for different scientists to come to different conclusions, even if they agree about some of the evidence. But there's more to it than that.

Presenter 1

Tell me more.

Presenter 2

It seems that other scientists simply couldn't imagine how massive continents could move across the planet. It was an **idea outside their experience**. Also, they didn't much respect Wegener – he was never regarded as a **member of the community of geologists**.

Presenter 1

And I suppose scientists don't give up their 'tried and tested' explanations easily?

Presenter 2

Exactly. Scientists often feel that it's safer to stick with **ideas that have served them well in the past**. Of course, new data that conflict with an explanation make scientists stop and think – but it could be that the data are incorrect, not the explanation! Generally, scientists only abandon an established explanation when there are really good reasons to do so, like someone suggesting a better one.

The scientific community

1 The stages below describe one way a scientific discovery is made and then reviewed by other scientists.

They are in the wrong order.

A   The scientist tells other scientists about the investigation results at a conference.

B   Other scientists try to reproduce the findings of the investigation.

C   If their findings are similar, it is more likely that other scientists will accept that the claim is correct.

D   Other scientists ask questions and evaluate the scientist's claims.

E   A scientist makes an unexpected observation.

F   The scientist does further investigations.

Fill in the boxes to show the right order. The first one has been done for you.

E					

2 Write a C next to reasons why two scientists may come to different conclusions about the same data.

Write an X next to reasons for scientists not abandoning an explanation even when new data do not seem to support the explanation.

a   The scientists are interested in different areas of science. ☐

b   The data may be incorrect. ☐

c   The new explanation may run into problems. ☐

d   Different organisations paid for each scientist's research. ☐

e   It is safer to stick with ideas that have served well in the past. ☐

> **Exam tip**
>
> Remember – a scientist's judgements may be influenced by their:
> • background
> • experience
> • interests
> • funding.

3 Below are eight answers. Make up one question for each answer.

Peer review

_____

Scientific conference

_____

Other scientists get similar results.

_____

The explanation has stood the test of time.

_____

Scientific journal

_____

A tobacco company employs one scientist; a cancer charity employs the other scientist.

_____

New data may be inaccurate.

_____

Different sponsors have paid for the research.

_____

4 Read the information in the box.

> It's not only fatty foods and smoking that are risk factors for heart disease! New research shows that decaffeinated coffee may also be bad for your heart. American scientists studied 187 people for three months. They found increased levels of harmful cholesterol in the blood of people who drank decaffeinated coffee. The researchers presented their findings to other scientists at the American Heart Association's conference.

Make up a dialogue on the next page to get across six important points about the scientific community.

Use the information in the box above and the phrases below.
- scientific journal or conference
- peer review
- evaluated by other scientists
- reproducible results
- different conclusions about the same data

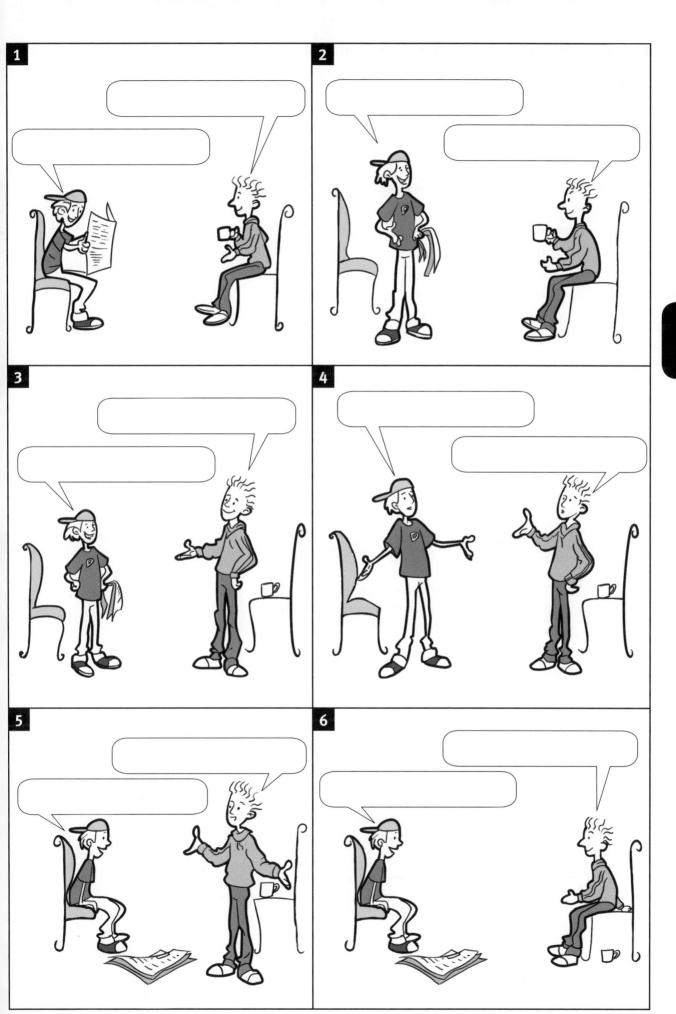

1 Read the information in the box opposite about the work of Charles Darwin in the 1860s.

Below are some statements from other scientists about Darwin's theory. Some statements are from 1870; others are from 2012.

A I don't know why there is variation within a species.

B There has not yet been time for other scientists to evaluate Darwin's ideas.

C DNA evidence explains how species are related to each other.

D I disagree with Darwin's theory. God created everything on Earth in seven days.

E We know that the Earth is about 4 thousand million years old.

F Darwin's observations are fine. But I don't know how living things pass on variations to their offspring.

G We often find new fossils, and we can date them accurately now.

H Darwin's theory has worked well for more than a hundred years.

I There is not enough fossil evidence to support Darwin's ideas.

J The Earth has not existed long enough for evolution to have happened.

K The data may be incorrect.

a Give the letters of four statements that show why many scientists in 1870 did not support Darwin's theory of natural selection.

_____ _____ _____ _____   [4]

b Give the letters of three statements that mention **evidence** that might make a 2012 scientist more likely to accept Darwin's theory than an 1870 scientist.

_____ _____ _____   [3]

c In 2030, a scientist collects data that seems to contradict Darwin's theory. He proposes a new explanation for evolution. Most scientists do not immediately accept the new explanation.

Give the letters of two statements that are reasons for scientists not accepting the new explanation.

_____ _____   [2]

Total [9]

Darwin collected evidence by making these observations:

- The individuals of a species are slightly different from each other. This is variation.
- There are always more members of a species than can survive. So there is competition between members of a species.

From his observations, Darwin developed his **theory of natural selection**:

- 'Any variation that helps an individual to survive is more likely to be inherited by its offspring'.

Darwin's theory helps to explain how and why evolution happens.

Exam tip

Remember that a good explanation:

- accounts for all the data
- might explain a link that people had not thought of before

2 Read the article below.

> ### Alcohol and the risk of heart disease
>
> Since the 1970s, research from many groups of scientists has suggested that drinking up to 30 g alcohol a day reduces the risk of heart disease. The researchers explained that alcohol helps prevents blood clots.
>
> In a 2005 study, a group of scientists claimed that drinking alcohol does not reduce the risk of heart disease. The scientists concluded that the reduced risk of heart disease in moderate drinkers could be caused by other factors. For example, 27 of 30 other risk factors for heart disease are higher in non-drinkers than in moderate drinkers.

4

a All the scientists who researched alcohol and heart disease published reports of their findings in scientific journals.

The reports include the scientists' investigation methods, their data, and their conclusions.

   i Other scientists looked carefully at the reports **before** they were published. Suggest why.

   _____ [1]

  ii Give two reasons for publishing reports in scientific journals.

   _____

   _____ [1]

b At first, many scientists did not accept the findings of the 2005 scientists. Suggest why.

  _____

  _____ [1]

c A second group of scientists collected data that suggests the same conclusion as the 2005 research.
How might the findings of the second group influence other scientists?
Tick the **one** best answer.

  Their findings make other scientists less likely to accept the claim of the 2005 scientists. ☐

  Their findings prove the claim of the 2005 scientists. ☐

  Their findings make other scientists more likely to question the claim of the 2005 scientists. ☐

  Their findings make other scientists more likely to accept the claim of the 2005 scientists. ☐

d Some organisations commented on the 2005 research findings.

Draw lines to match each comment to an organisation that might have made the comment.

Organisation		Comment
Wine-making company		Just two studies show that moderate drinking does not reduce the risk of heart disease. Many more studies show the opposite. People can continue drinking as usual.
Organisation that persuades people not to drink alcohol		We need more information before we can assess whether the claim of the 2005 research is correct. We want more scientists to do research about the impact of alcohol on heart health.
European health organisation		The 2005 study shows that the results of the earlier research could well be wrong. People who drink alcohol are not protecting themselves against heart disease.

3 Read the information in the box.
Then answer the questions below.

> **Finding out about the origin of the atmosphere**
>
> Scientists have collected data about:
> - the ages of rocks
> - the chemicals rocks are made of
> - fossils of early plants and animals.
>
> Scientists have interpreted the data, and used the data to come up with an explanation about the origin of the atmosphere.
>
> Very recently, scientists found fossils of animals that are more than 50 million years older than any other known animal fossils.

Use examples from the box to help you:

a   explain why scientists may come up with different
    explanations based on the same data

    _____

    _____ [3]

b   describe what scientists may do when they find new data
    that disagrees with an accepted explanation.

    _____

    _____ [3]

                                            Total [6]

4   a   Tick the **two** reasons below that best explain why a
            scientist may decide to tell others about their research
            findings at a scientific conference.

            So that other scientists can talk about the
            findings on television.   ☐

            So that other scientists can write about the
            findings in a scientific journal.   ☐

            So that other scientists can try to reproduce
            the findings in future.   ☐

            So that other scientists can ask questions
            about the findings.   ☐   [2]

b   In 1912, Alfred Wegener presented his idea of continental
        drift to other scientists at a conference in Germany.

        i   List three pieces of evidence Wegener used to support
                his idea.

                _____

                _____

                _____ [3]

        ii Explain why most scientists at the conference did not
                accept Wegener's idea.

                _____

                _____

                _____ [3]

4

iii Today, most geologists accept the scientific explanation that continents drift because of the movement of tectonic plates.

Tick the **two** reasons that best explain why geologists now accept this explanation, even though it was rejected in 1912.

Data collected since 1912 support the explanation. ☐

The Earth's crust is made up of about 12 tectonic plates. ☐

The Earth's crust is thin compared to the mantle and the core. ☐

Data collected since 1912 agree with predictions based on the explanation. ☐

[2]

Total [10]

Risk

> Don't buy that cereal. It's far too salty. We don't want to risk the kids getting high blood pressure. Too much salt might increase the risk of asthma, too.

> But **nothing is risk free**. Many scientific advances introduce new risks. What about their vaccination this afternoon? It might prevent meningitis C, but there is a risk of side-effects.

> True, but there is only a tiny chance of a serious side-effect from the vaccine. There is a much higher chance of getting high blood pressure from eating too much salt over the years.

5

> Why are you lying out there in the sun at midday? Where's your sunscreen? It's dangerous to sunbathe – ultraviolet radiation from the sun hugely increases your chance of getting skin cancer. Each year, nearly 6000 British people get melanoma skin cancer. And skin cancer kills.

> Yes, but there are **benefits** too. Sunlight helps you make vitamin D. You need this to strengthen your bones and muscles, and to boost your immune system. Anyway, I feel more confident when I've got a tan. And it's lovely and warm out here...

> OK. I guess it's up to you. No one is forcing you to take the risk. But think of the consequences of getting skin cancer. And the costs to the NHS of treating you. We'll all pay in the end.

1

The government is planning to build new nuclear power stations. A spokesperson says that they will safeguard future electricity supplies without contributing to global warming.

2

Well, they'd better not build one near here. I'm moving if they do.

*What's your problem? The **chance** of a nuclear power station exploding is tiny.*

3

*But you've got to think of the **consequences** if it did explode. Two and a half thousand people died after the 1986 accident at Chernobyl.*

And don't forget the risk of radioactive materials leaking out.

4

*You're getting confused here. The **statistically estimated risk** of a leak is very low. I reckon you are **over-estimating** the risks because ionising radiation – and its effects – are invisible, and you're not used to it.*

5

We've not even mentioned nuclear waste! We can't possibly know about the effects of this over the next thousand years.

Exactly. The government must not build them.

6

I disagree. It is the job of the government to weigh up the risks and benefits to everyone involved. It must assess what level of risk is acceptable. Then it must make a decision – even if you don't like it!

Risk

1 Use the clues to fill in the grid.

1 Everything we do carries a risk of accident or h . . .

2 We can assess the size of a risk by measuring the c . . . of it happening in a large sample over a certain time.

3 New vaccines are an example of a scientific a . . . that brings with it new risks.

4 Radioactive materials emit i . . . radiation all the time.

5 The chance of a nuclear power station exploding is small. The c . . . of this happening would be devastating.

6 Governments or public bodies may have to a . . . what level of risk is acceptable in a particular situation.

7 Some decisions about risk may be c . . ., especially if those most at risk are not those who benefit.

8 Sometimes people think the size of a risk is bigger than it really is. Their perception of the size of the risk is greater than the s . . . calculated risk.

9 Nuclear power stations emit less carbon dioxide than coal-fired power stations. Some people think that this b . . . is worth the risk of building nuclear power stations.

10 Many people think that the size of the risk of flying in an aeroplane is greater than it really is. They p . . . that flying is risky because they don't fly very often.

11 It is impossible to reduce risk to zero. So people must decide what level of risk is a . . .

5

2 Draw a line to link two words on the circle.
Write a sentence on the line saying how the two words
are connected.
Repeat for as many pairs as you can.

risk

safe   benefits

chance   consequences

balance   unfamiliar

scientific advances   long-lasting effects

statistically estimated risk   perceived risk

controversial

Risk

1 A group of friends are talking about using mobile phones.

Catherine

> I use my phone all the time to talk to family and friends. I'm not worried about microwave radiation from the phone. My skull absorbs most of it.

Zion

> I was worried about microwaves from my phone heating up my brain cells and damaging them. So now I use my hands-free set.

Junaid

Sarah

> Running for half an hour heats your brain up more than mobile phone radiation. I won't use my phone any less.

> I read a 2011 report from the World Health Organization. It says that mobile phone radiation may cause cancer. So I text everyone now.

5

a Which two people are taking action to reduce the risks from exposure to radiation from mobile phones?

Put ticks (✔) in the boxes next to the two correct names.

Catherine ☐

Sarah ☐

Zion ☐

Junaid ☐ [1]

b Which three people are talking about the hazards from exposure to radiation from mobile phones?

Put ticks (✔) in the boxes next to the three correct names.

Catherine ☐

Sarah ☐

Zion ☐

Junaid ☐ [1]

c Which person mentions something that prevents mobile phone radiation reaching the brain?

Put a tick (✔) in the box next to the correct name.

Catherine ☐

Sarah ☐

Zion ☐

Junaid ☐ [1]

Total [3]

2 Research shows that using sunbeds increases the risk of developing skin cancer. Ultraviolet radiation from sunbeds can cause eye cancer.

Some people who use sunbeds suffer from dry, bumpy, or itchy skin.

Many people use sunbeds in tanning shops regularly.

a One tanning shop displays this notice.

Using our sunbeds

- Lock the door. ☐

- Wear goggles. ☐

- Use the sunbed for a maximum of 15 minutes. ☐

- Wipe the sunbed clean after use. ☐

- Return your towel to reception. ☐

- Do not use the sunbed if you have lots of moles or freckles. ☐

Some of the information describes ways of reducing the risks of using sunbeds.

Write **R** in **three** boxes next to sentences that describe ways of reducing the risks from ultraviolet radiation. [3]

b **i** Suggest one reason why many people are willing to accept the risks of using sunbeds.

_____

_____ [1]

ii Three people made these comments about the risks of using sunbeds.

A I reckon the risk of getting skin cancer from sunbeds is tiny. My mum uses them all the time. She wouldn't if they were dangerous!

B I read an article in a medical journal. It says that the risk of developing skin cancer increases by 20% for every ten years you use sunbeds.

C Sunbeds are really dangerous. Your skin can go red and itchy when you use them. You can get eye cancer from them really quickly, too.

Give the letter of **one** comment that identifies a statistically calculated risk of using sunbeds.

_____

Give the letter of **one** comment that identifies a **perceived** risk of using sunbeds. _____ [2]

c A Member of Parliament (MP) wants to ban sunbeds.

Use ideas about risk, benefit, and balance to discuss possible reasons for the MP wanting to ban sunbeds.

_____

_____

_____

_____

_____

_____ [3]

Total [9]

3 Human activities cause an increase in greenhouse gases, such as carbon dioxide. Increasing amounts of greenhouse gases lead to global warming. Global warming causes rising sea levels and flooding.

The graphs show how greenhouse gas emissions from the USA and the European Union changed between 1990 and 2000.

5

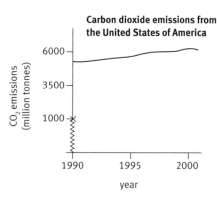

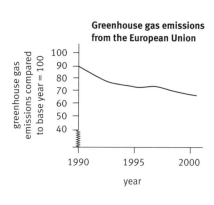

a Describe the trend for the European Union.

_____

_____ [1]

b Complete the sentences.

Use words from this list.

benefits	chances	consequences	precautions

If all countries have a similar trend to the USA, the
_____that the Earth's temperature will continue
to increase are high. The _____ of this for people
who live on low-lying islands could be devastating.   [2]

Total [3]

4 Read the information in the box.

Mephedrone is an illegal drug. It is similar to cocaine. It began
to be widely used in 2007. It was banned in the UK in 2010. In 2011,
the government reported that about 4.4% of 16–14-year-olds had
used the drug as during the past year.

Mephedrone makes some users feel happy for up to 3 hours.

The drug has many side-effects. The bar charts show the findings
from two surveys on the side-effects of taking mephedrone.

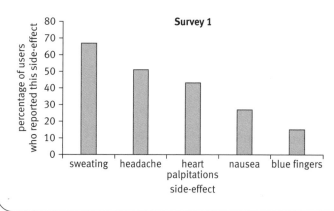

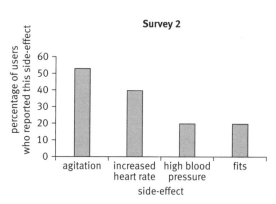

Little is known about the long-term effects of taking the drug, or about its effects when taken in combination with other drugs. One user was admitted to a psychiatric hospital after taking the drug for 18 months.

a   Suggest two reasons that people may give for taking mephedrone, even though it is illegal and there are many risks associated with taking the drug.

_____

_____ [2]

b   Kyle uses mephedrone.

He tells a radio programme, "It is my choice to use mephedrone. There are no known long-term risks. The short-term risks are ones that I am prepared to take."

Identify two reasons for Kyle's willingness to accept the risks of taking mephedrone.

_____

_____ [2]

c   Suggest why little is known about the long-term effects of taking mephedrone.

_____

_____ [1]

d   i   From the bar charts, identify the one short-term effect that a user of mephedrone has the smallest chance of experiencing.

_____ [1]

   ii   Use the bar charts to identify the three side-effects that a user of mephedrone has the highest chance of experiencing.

_____ [1]

e   Suggest why the government made mephedrone illegal in 2011, rather than leaving to individuals the decision of whether or not to risk taking the drug.

_____

_____ [1]

Total [8]

5

5 Read the information in the box.

a The recommended maximum daily salt intake for an adult is 6 g a day.

Use the table above to work out the mass of bread that contains this mass of salt.

Answer = _____ g   [2]

b i Oliver has high blood pressure.

His doctor tells him to cut down on salt to reduce his risk of heart disease.

Oliver wants to choose a low-salt breakfast to have every day. Should he choose 75 g of bread with 10 g of spread **or** 50 g of rice flakes with 200 g milk?

Show your working to help explain your answer.   [4]

ii Explain why eating porridge every day (made from oats and milk) would further reduce the risk of Oliver getting heart disease.

_____   [1]

c Many people like salty food. Even so, some food manufacturers have reduced the amount of salt in the foods they make. Suggest why.

_____   [1]

d The British government is working with the food industry to reduce salt levels in food, but has not made food with high levels of salt illegal. Suggest why.

_____

_____   [1]

Total [9]

There is strong evidence that eating too much salt is linked to high blood pressure. High blood pressure is the main cause of strokes, and a major cause of heart disease. Diets high in salt may also cause stomach cancer, and make asthma symptoms worse.

The table shows the amount of salt in some foods.

Food	Mass of salt in 100 g of food (g)
bread	1.5
spread	1.4
porridge oats	trace
rice flakes breakfast cereal	1.2
milk	0.04

Making decisions about science and technology

1

It's 2011. People are protesting against a proposed new palm oil power station. A journalist is interviewing one of the protesters.

> *So why are you against biofuels? Surely burning palm oil to generate electricity is more **sustainable** than burning fossil fuels. There will be more fossil fuels for future generations. Isn't that a **benefit** of biofuels?*

2

> *True, but there are **unintended impacts** too. In Indonesia, companies evict local people and destroy tropical rainforests to make space to grow oil palms. Vital habitats are lost forever. Biodiversity is reduced. In my opinion, this can never be **ethically** right.*

3

> *So I guess there are **benefits** and **costs**, and we need to weigh them up. What about jobs for people here in Britain?*

4

> *Well, the palm oil power station would employ 30 people. But weigh that against increased emissions of oxides of nitrogen from burning palm oil. They worsen asthma and other lung diseases. Is that good for Britain?*

5

> *And one other impact. Scientists have collected data about carbon dioxide emissions. Burning rainforests to grow oil palms emits thousands of times as much carbon dioxide as can be prevented by using palm oil. So **NO TO THE BIOFUEL PLANT!***

6

ctbank

2

...zerland they recycle about ...ypes of plastic waste. Here in ...uch less. Why the difference?

Well, of course it's **technically possible** for the USA to recycle as much plastic as the Swiss. But we Americans choose to recycle less. I guess it's a question of **values**, not science. We can't expect scientists to answer questions about values!

You mean people in the US are too lazy to sort out their plastic rubbish?

Partly that. Governments' values matter too. Perhaps the Swiss government is more worried about landfill sites, or the pollutants that come from burning waste. And don't forget finances; the USA chooses not to spend money on sorting, cleaning, and transporting plastic rubbish.

3

It's like my grandparents. They didn't have much money, so they used things again and again. 'Waste not, want not,' they used to say.

Of course! It's **economics**. When people have less money, they reuse things more.

And it depends on the **social context**. We live in a 'throwaway society'. It wasn't like that so much when my grandparents were young.

Debating Society: 18 March

Is it ethically acceptable to clone human embryos to produce stem cells to treat illnesses?

1

I will start with a short explanation. Embryonic stem cells are cells that are not yet specialised; they can develop into any type of cell. To obtain embryonic stem cells, scientists create embryos in the lab. They harvest stem cells from the embryos. Then they destroy what's left of the embryos.

2

I believe that that, ethically, the process is totally unacceptable. Life begins at conception. It is always wrong and unnatural to create and destroy embryos in the lab. I believe this even though I know that stem cell therapy may greatly benefit some people.

3

As we have just heard, stem cell therapy has many likely benefits. Stem cells could provide tissue for an organ transplant to save someone's life. They could treat heart disease or diabetes.

4

So what do you think, ethically?

6

5

*I believe that the right decision is the one that leads to the **best outcome for the majority of people involved**. So if many people will benefit greatly, it is right to go ahead with researching stem cell treatments.*

6

Even if some people – or embryos – suffer?

No.

Yes.

...ıs about science and

...xt to the questions that science could answer.

...itain build more nuclear power stations, or
...rate on renewable energy resources instead? ☐

...nuclear power meet all Britain's current
...gy needs? ☐

...at techniques for cloning stem cells are successful? ☐

...Should the MMR vaccination be compulsory? ☐

How much NO_x pollution does burning palm oil add
to the atmosphere? ☐

F How much plastic waste could be recycled in Britain? ☐

G If an AIDS vaccine were available, who should be
given it? ☐

H What percentage of children who get the MMR
vaccine get ill with measles? ☐

I Is it ethically right to clone stem cells to treat disease? ☐

J Should Britain recycle more of its plastic waste? ☐

K Is it possible to develop an AIDS vaccine? ☐

L Do the benefits of wind power outweigh the
disadvantages? ☐

Exam tip

Science can answer questions
about what **could** be done.
But it cannot answer questions
about what **should** be done.
These may be linked to ethics,
economics, or social context.

2 Use the words in the box to fill in the gaps in the
sentences below.

| quality | benefits | environment | unintended |
| weigh | value |

Science-based technology provides us with many things we

_____ . But some applications of science have _____

impacts on the _____ of life and the _____ .

When we make a decision about an application of science, we

need to _____ up the costs and _____ .

3 Find 12 words from this Ideas about science section in the wordsearch. Then write a crossword clue for each word.

S	S	N	O	I	T	S	E	U	Q	T
U	N	A	R	V	B	R	I	S	K	E
S	O	S	C	I	E	N	C	E	I	C
T	I	E	E	E	N	Q	S	E	N	H
A	T	V	Y	W	E	U	I	G	S	N
I	A	O	A	S	F	T	E	L	E	I
N	L	L	A	C	I	H	T	E	U	C
A	U	N	N	A	T	U	R	A	L	A
B	G	L	C	O	S	T	S	X	A	L
L	E	L	B	I	S	A	E	F	V	L
E	R	I	M	A	J	O	R	I	T	Y

6

Word	Clue

4 Read the information in the box about values and ethics in science.

Then make notes about values and ethics in science in the table.
- Write a title in the top row.
- Write the two or three most important points in the next row down.
- Write other, detailed, information in the lowest three rows.

> There are many questions that cannot be addressed using a scientific approach. For example, a scientist can find out how to get stem cells from embryos, and how to use the stem cells to treat diseases. But people have different views about whether it is ethically right to actually use these techniques. So it is up to others – not just scientists – to answer the question *'is it ethically acceptable to use embryonic stem cells to treat disease?'*
>
> People use different sorts of arguments when they discuss ethical issues. One argument is that the right decision is the one that gives the best outcome for the greatest number of people involved. Another argument is that some actions are always right or wrong, whatever the consequences.

Title:	
Most important points:	
Other information:	

Making decisions about science and technology

1 a An electricity company needs to decide whether to build a new nuclear power station or a coal-fired power station.

The company asks people from five organisations for their opinions.

Freya   Electricity from coal and nuclear power stations costs about the same.

Grace   Coal power stations produce acid rain. This damages trees.

Hari   Nuclear power stations produce less carbon dioxide than coal power stations. Carbon dioxide is a greenhouse gas.

Ian   There is no risk-free way of disposing of nuclear waste. A nuclear waste leak could make land unsuitable for farming for hundreds of years.

Jasmine   A nuclear accident could kill thousands. It is not right to put people at such a risk.

Kris   If we build a nuclear power station, there will be more coal left for people in future.

i Write the names of two people whose opinions are linked to the idea of sustainability.

_____ and _____ [2]

ii Write the names of two people whose opinions show that they are concerned about the environment.

_____ and _____ [2]

iii Write the name of one person who is giving an ethical argument.

_____ [1]

b Old nuclear power stations must be taken down. This process is called decommissioning.

Tick the boxes next to the jobs that are likely to be part of the work of an official organisation that regulates the decommissioning of nuclear power stations.

Making sure used fuel rods are disposed of safely.   ☐

Deciding whether to build new nuclear or new gas-fired power stations   ☐

6

Regularly checking storage sites where low-level and intermediate radioactive waste are stored. ☐

Deciding which countries to buy nuclear fuelw from. ☐ [2]

Total [7]

2 Pre-implantation genetic screening (PGS) is a technique to choose the best embryo to implant in a woman who is having fertility treatment.

The technique involves removing one cell from an eight-cell embryo.
Scientists then test this cell for abnormal chromosomes.
Abnormal chromosomes may cause conditions like Down's syndrome.

a Five people were asked for their opinions about PGS. Some people support the technique; others think it should not be allowed.

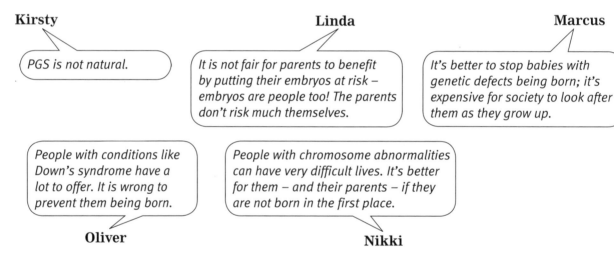

Kirsty
PGS is not natural.

Linda
It is not fair for parents to benefit by putting their embryos at risk – embryos are people too! The parents don't risk much themselves.

Marcus
It's better to stop babies with genetic defects being born; it's expensive for society to look after them as they grow up.

People with conditions like Down's syndrome have a lot to offer. It is wrong to prevent them being born.
Oliver

People with chromosome abnormalities can have very difficult lives. It's better for them – and their parents – if they are not born in the first place.
Nikki

Write the names of the people in the correct columns in the table.

People who *agree* with pre-implantation genetic screening	People who *disagree* with pre-implantation genetic screening

[3]

b Write **S** next to the questions that could be answered using a scientific approach.

Write **V** next to the questions that address issues of **values** of PGS.

Is PGS ethically acceptable? ☐

Does the technique damage embryos? ☐

Is it natural to choose which embryo to implant in a woman's uterus? ☐

Do embryos that have been tested grow properly when they are implanted into a woman's uterus? ☐

Is PGS necessary – maybe embryos can fix their own genetic defects? ☐

Is it right to destroy embryos that are not implanted? ☐ [3]

c Suggest two reasons why PGS is offered to parents in the UK but is not offered to parents in some other countries.

_____

_____

_____ [2]

Total [8]

6

3 Sustainability means using resources to meet the needs of people today without damaging the Earth or reducing the resources for people in future.

A power station in Bristol burns hospital waste to generate electricity.

a Suggest one way in which generating electricity from hospital waste is more sustainable than simply burning hospital waste.

_____

_____ [1]

b It is technically possible to use waste from all British hospitals to generate electricity.

However, waste from only a few hospitals is used in this way.

Suggest two reasons for this.

_____

_____

_____ [2]

Total [3]

4 A British company wants to buy a large area of rainforest from a government of a poorer country.

It plans to clear the rainforest and use the land to grow oil palms.

It will transport palm oil to Britain.

In Britain, the palm oil will be burned to generate electricity.

- Summarise the benefits and costs the government might consider when deciding whether or not to sell the rainforest to the British company.
- On balance, do you think the government should sell the rainforest? Give reasons to support your decision.

✎ The quality of written communication will be assessed in your answer to this question.

Write your answer on separate paper or in your exercise book.

Total [6]

> **Exam tip**
>
> Before starting to write your answer to questions like the one above, make notes of the benefits and costs. Organise your notes, and decide on your decision. Then write your answer, based on these notes. Finally, check your answer and correct any mistakes of spelling, punctuation, or grammar.

5 All British babies are offered the MMR vaccine against measles, mumps, and rubella.

Some parents decide not to have their babies vaccinated.

a Give one reason why some people think that parents should be free to choose whether or not their baby gets the MMR vaccine.

_____

_____

_____ [1]

b Give one reason why some people think that the MMR vaccine should be compulsory.

_____

_____

_____ [1]

Total [2]

absorb (radiation) The radiation that hits an object and is not reflected, or transmitted through it, is absorbed (for example, black paper absorbs light). Its energy makes the object get a little hotter.

accumulate To collect together and increase in quantity.

accuracy How close a quantitative result is to the true or 'actual' value.

adaptation A feature that helps an organism survive in its environment.

ADH A hormone that makes kidney tubules more permeable to water, causing greater re-absorption of water.

aerial A wire, or arrangement of wires, that emits radio waves when there is an alternating current in it, and in which an alternating current is induced by passing radio waves. So it acts as a source or a receiver of radio waves.

alcohol The intoxicating chemical in wine, beer, and spirits. Causes changes in behaviour and may create long-term addiction.

alkali A compound that dissolves in water to give a solution with a pH higher than 7. An alkali can be neutralised by an acid to form a salt.

alkali A compound that dissolves in water to give a solution with a pH higher than 7. An alkali can be neutralised by an acid to form a salt. Solutions of alkalis contain hydroxide ions.

Alkali Acts The Acts of Parliament passed in the UK in order to control levels of pollution. They led to the formation of an Alkali Inspectorate, which checked that at least 95% of acid fumes were removed from the chimneys of chemical factories.

allele Different versions of the same gene.

amplifier A device for increasing the amplitude of an electrical signal. Used in radios and other audio equipment.

amplitude For a mechanical wave, the maximum distance that each point on the medium moves from its normal position as the wave passes. For an electromagnetic wave, the maximum value of the varying electric field (or magnetic field).

analogue signal Signals used in communications in which the amplitude can vary continuously.

antibiotic resistant Microorganisms that are not killed by antibiotics.

antibiotics Drugs that kill or stop the growth of bacteria and fungi.

antibodies A group of proteins made by white blood cells to fight dangerous microorganisms. A different antibody is needed to fight each different type of microorganism. Antibodies bind to the surface of the microorganism, which triggers other white blood cells to digest them.

antigens The proteins on the surface of a cell. A cell's antigens are unique markers.

artery A blood vessel that carries blood away from the heart.

asexual reproduction When a new individual is produced from just one parent.

assumption A piece of information that is taken for granted without sufficient evidence to be certain.

asteroid A dwarf rocky planet, generally orbiting the Sun between the orbits of Mars and Jupiter.

atmosphere The layer of gases that surrounds the Earth.

atom The smallest particle of an element. The atoms of each element are the same as each other and are different from the atoms of other elements.

best estimate When measuring a variable, the value in which you have most confidence.

big bang An explosion of a single mass of material. This is currently the accepted scientific explanation for the start of the Universe.

biodegradable Materials that are broken down in the environment by microorganisms. Most synthetic polymers are not biodegradable.

biodiversity The great variety of living things, both within a species and between different species.

biofuel A renewable fuel that uses biological material, such as recently living plant materials and animal waste.

bleach A chemical that can destroy unwanted colours. Bleaches also kill bacteria. A common bleach is a solution of chlorine in sodium hydroxide.

blind trial A clinical trial in which the patient does not know whether they are taking the new drug, but their doctor does.

blood pressure The pressure exerted by blood pushing on the walls of a blood vessel.

blood transfusion Transfer of blood from one person to another.

branched chain A chain of carbon atoms with short side branches.

brine A solution of sodium chloride (salt) in water. Brine is produced by solution mining of underground salt deposits.

(H) calculated risk Risk calculated from reliable data.

capillary The smallest blood vessel. Its walls are only one cell thick and allow substances to diffuse between the blood and the cells.

carbon cycle The cycling of the element carbon in the environment between the atmosphere, biosphere, hydrosphere, and lithosphere. The element exists in different compounds in these spheres. In the atmosphere it is mainly present as carbon dioxide.

carrier Someone who has the recessive allele for a characteristic or disease but who does not have the characteristic or disease itself.

carrier wave A steady stream of radio waves produced by an RF oscillator in a radio to carry information.

catalyst A chemical that speeds up a chemical reaction but is not used up in the process.

catalytic converter A device fitted to a vehicle exhaust that changes the waste gases into less harmful ones.

cause When there is evidence that changes in a factor produce a particular outcome, then the factor is said to cause the outcome. For example, increases in the pollen count cause increases in the incidence of hayfever.

ceramic Solid material such as pottery, glass, cement, and brick.

CFCs Liquids that used to be used in refrigerators and aerosols. Their vapour damages the ozone layer.

chemical change/chemical reaction A change that forms a new chemical.

chemical equation A summary of a chemical reaction showing the reactants and products with their physical states (see balanced chemical equation).

chemical formula A way of describing a chemical that uses symbols for atoms. It gives information about the number of different types of atom in the chemical.

(H) chemical synthesis Making a new chemical by joining together simpler chemicals.

chlorination The process of adding chlorine to water to kill microorganisms, so that it is safe to drink.

chlorine A greenish toxic gas, used to bleach paper and textiles, and to treat water.

(H) chlorofluorocarbons (CFCs) Liquids that used to be used in refrigerators and aerosols. Their vapour damages the ozone layer.

chromosome Long, thin, threadlike structure in the nucleus of a cell made from a molecule of DNA. Chromosomes carry the genes.

classification Putting living things into groups based on their shared characteristics.

climate Average weather in a region over many years.

clinical trial When a new drug is tested on humans to find out whether it is safe and whether it works.

clone A new cell or individual made by asexual reproduction. A clone has the same genes as its parent.

combustion The process of burning a substance that reacts with oxygen to produce heat and light.

comet A rocky lump, held together by frozen gases and water, that orbits the Sun in a highly elliptical orbit.

competition Different organisms that require the same resource, such as water, food, light, or space, must compete for the resource.

compression A material is in compression when forces are trying to push it together and make it smaller.

(H) computer model A computer uses data and equations to study events that have happened or to predict what might happen.

concentration The quantity of a chemical dissolved in a stated volume of solution. Concentrations can be measured in grams per litre.

condensed The change of state from a gas to a liquid, for example, water vapour in the air condenses to form rain.

conservation of atoms All the atoms present at the beginning of a chemical reaction are still there at the end. No new atoms are created and no atoms are destroyed during a chemical reaction.

conservation of energy The principle that the total amount of energy at the end of any process is always equal to the total amount of energy at the beginning – though it may now be stored in different ways and in different places.

conservation of mass The total mass of chemicals is the same at the end of a reaction as at the beginning. No atoms are created or destroyed and so no mass is gained or lost.

consumer An organism that eats others in a food chain. This is all the organisms in a food chain except the producer(s).

contamination Having a radioactive material inside the body, or having it on the skin or clothes.

continental drift A theory that describes the extremely slow movements of the continents across the Earth.

control In a clinical trial, the control group is people taking the currently used drug. The effects of the new drug can then be compared to this group.

convection The movement that occurs when hot material rises and cooler material sinks.

core The Earth's core is made mostly from iron, solid at the centre and liquid above.

coronary artery The artery that supplies blood carrying oxygen and glucose directly to the muscle cells of the heart.

correlation A link between two things. For example, if an outcome happens when a factor is present, but not when it is absent, or if an outcome increases or decreases when a factor increases. For example, when pollen count increases hayfever cases also increase.

cross-link A link or bond joining polymer chains together.

crude oil A dark, oily liquid found in the Earth, which is a mixture of hydrocarbons.

crust A rocky layer at the surface of the Earth, 10–40 km deep.

crystalline polymer A polymer with molecules lined up in a regular way as in a crystal.

crystallise To form crystals, for example, by evaporating the water from a solution of a salt.

cystic fibrosis An inherited disorder. The disorder is caused by recessive alleles.

decommissioning Taking a power station out of service at the end of its lifetime, dismantling it, and disposing of the waste safely.

decomposer bacteria Microorganisms that break down the organic compounds in dead plants and animals and waste.

decomposition The process of breaking down dead plants and animals and waste by microorganisms.

deforestation Cutting down trees from an area of land.

(H) denitrification The removal of nitrogen from soil. Bacteria break down nitrates in the soil, converting them back to nitrogen.

(H) denitrifying bacteria Bacteria that break down nitrates in the soil, releasing nitrogen into the air.

density A dense material is heavy for its size. Density is mass divided by volume.

detector Any device or instrument that shows the presence of radiation by absorbing it.

(H) detritivore An organism that feeds on dead organisms and waste. Woodlice, earthworms, and millipedes are examples of detritivores.

digest To break down larger, insoluble molecules into small, soluble molecules.

digital code A string of 0s and 1s that can be used to represent an analogue signal, and from which that signal can be reconstructed.

digital signal Signals used in communications in which the amplitude can take only one of two values, corresponding to the digits 0 and 1.

disease A condition that impairs normal functioning of an organism's body, usually associated with particular signs and symptoms. It may be caused by an infection or by the dysfunction of internal organs.

dissolve Some chemicals Mix with liquids (solvents) to form solutions. Salt and sugar, for example, dissolve in water.

DNA (deoxyribonucleic acid) The chemical that makes up chromosomes. DNA carries the genetic code, which controls how an organism develops.

dominant Describes an allele that will show up in an organism even if a different allele of the gene is present. You only need to have one copy of a dominant allele to have the feature it produces.

(H) double-blind trial A clinical trial in which neither the doctor nor the patient knows whether the patient is taking the new drug.

durable A material is durable if it lasts a long time in use. It does not wear out.

duration How long something happens for. For example, the length of time someone is exposed to radiation.

dwarf planet A round, planetlike object with a similar orbit to the eight planets but too small to clear its orbit of other small objects.

earthquake An event in which rocks break to allow tectonic plate movement, causing the ground to shake.

economic context How money changes hands between businesses, government, and individuals.

Ecstasy A recreational drug that increases the concentration of serotonin at the synapses in the brain, giving pleasurable feelings. Long-term effects may include destruction of the synapses.

effector The part of a control system that brings about a change to the system.

efficiency The percentage of the energy supplied to a device that is transferred to the desired place, or in the desired way.

electric current A flow of charge around an electric circuit.

electrolysis Splitting up a chemical into its elements by passing an electric current through it.

electromagnetic induction The name of the process in which a potential difference (and hence often an electric current) is generated in a wire, when it is in a changing magnetic field.

electromagnetic spectrum The 'family' of electromagnetic waves of different frequencies and wavelengths.

electromagnetic wave A wave consisting of vibrating electric and magnetic fields, which can travel in a vacuum. Visible light is one example.

embryo The earliest stage of development for an animal or plant. In humans the embryo stage lasts for the first two months.

emission Something given out by something else, for example, the emission of carbon dioxide from combustion engines.

emit Give out (radiation).

endangered A species that is at risk of becoming extinct.

energy cost The amount of energy used to produce something or to do something.

environment Everything that surrounds you. This is factors like the air and water, as well as other living things.

enzyme A protein that catalyses (speeds up) chemical reactions in living things.

epidemiological study A scientific study that examines the causes, spread, and control of a disease in a human population.

erosion The movement of solids at the Earth's surface (for example, soil, mud, and rock) caused by wind, water, ice, and gravity, and living organisms.

ethics A set of principles that may show how to behave in a situation.

evaporate The change of state from a liquid to a gas.

evolution The process by which species gradually change over time. Evolution can produce new species.

excretion The removal of waste products of chemical reactions from cells.

extinct A species is extinct when all the members of the species have died out.

extruded A plastic is shaped by being forced through a mould.

factor A variable that changes and may affect something else.

false negative A wrong test result. The test result says that a person does not have a medical condition but this is incorrect.

false positive A wrong test result. The test result says that a person has a medical condition but this is incorrect.

fertile An organism that can produce offspring.

fibres Long thin threads that make up materials such as wool and polyester. Most fibres used for textiles consist of natural or synthetic polymers.

filter To separate a solid from a liquid by passing it through a filter paper.

filtering Separating a solid from a liquid by passing it through a filter paper.

flavouring Mixtures of chemicals that give food, sweets, toothpaste, and other products their flavours.

flexible A flexible material bends easily without breaking.

food chain A diagram that shows what organisms eat, with arrows showing how energy flows through the chain. A food chain always starts with a plant.

food web A series of linked food chains showing the feeding relationships in a habitat – 'what eats what'.

formula (chemical) A way of describing a chemical that uses symbols for atoms. A formula gives information about the numbers of different types of atom in the chemical. The formula of sulfuric acid, for example, is H_2SO_4.

fossil fuel Natural gas, oil, or coal.

fossil The stony remains of an animal or plant that lived millions of years ago, or an imprint it has made (for example, a footprint) in a surface.

fraction A mixture of hydrocarbons with similar boiling points that have been separated from crude oil by fractional distillation.

fractional distillation The process of separating crude oil into groups of molecules with similar boiling points called fractions.

frequency The frequency of a wave is the number of waves that pass any point each second.

functional protein Proteins that take part in chemical reactions, for example, enzymes.

fungi A group of living things, including some microorganisms, that cannot make their own food.

galaxy A collection of thousands of millions of stars held together by gravity.

gamma radiation (gamma rays) The most penetrating type of ionising radiation, produced by the nucleus of an atom in radioactive decay. The most energetic part of the electromagnetic spectrum.

gene A section of DNA giving instructions for a cell about how to make one kind of protein.

generator A device used to produce electricity by spinning a magnet near a coil of wire (or a coil near a magnet).

genetic screening Testing a population for a particular allele.

genetic study A scientific study of the genes carried by people in a population to look for alleles that increase the risk of disease.

genetic test A test to find whether a person has a particular DNA sequence or allele.

genetic variation The differences between individuals caused by differences in their genes. Gametes show genetic variation – they all have different genes.

Ⓗ genotype A description of the genes an organism has.

geothermal power station A power station that uses energy from hot underground rocks to heat water to produce steam to drive turbines.

grain A relatively small particle of a substance, for example, grains of sand.

greenhouse effect The atmosphere absorbs infrared radiation from the Earth's surface and radiates some of it back to the surface, making it warmer than it would otherwise be.

greenhouse gas A gas that contributes to the greenhouse effect, including carbon dioxide, methane, and water vapour.

habitat The place where an organism lives.

hard A material that is difficult to dent or scratch.

heart disease A disease where the coronary arteries become increasingly blocked with fatty deposits, restricting the blood flow to the heart muscle. The risk of this is increased by a high fat diet, smoking, and drinking excess alcohol.

Ⓗ heterozygous An individual with two different alleles for a particular gene.

homeostasis Keeping a steady state inside your body.

Ⓗ homozygous An individual with both alleles of a particular gene the same.

human trial The stage of the trial process for a new drug where the drug is taken by healthy volunteers to see if it is safe, and then by sick volunteers to check that it works.

Huntington's disease An inherited disease of the nervous system. The symptoms do not show up until middle age.

hydrocarbon A compound of hydrogen and carbon only. Ethane, C_2H_6, is a hydrocarbon.

hydroelectric power station A power station that uses water stored behind a dam to drive turbines to generate electricity.

hydrogen chloride gas An acid gas that is toxic and corrosive, and is produced by the Leblanc process.

hydrogen sulfide gas A poisonous gas that smells of rotten eggs.

immune Able to react to an infection quickly, stopping the microorganisms before they can make you ill, usually because you've been exposed to them before.

immune system A group of organs and tissues in the body that fight infections.

incinerator A factory for burning rubbish, which may generate electricity.

indirectly When something humans do affects another species, but this wasn't the reason for the action. For example, a species habitat is destroyed when land is cleared for farming.

infectious A disease that can be caught. The microorganism that causes it is passed from one person to another through the air, through water, or by touch.

infertile An organism that cannot produce offspring.

information (in a computer) Data stored and processed. It is measured in bytes.

infrared Electromagnetic waves with a frequency lower than that of visible light, beyond the red end of the visible spectrum.

inherited A feature that is passed from parents to offspring by their genes.

intensity The intensity of a beam of electromagnetic radiation is the energy arriving at a square metre of surface each second.

interdependence The relationships between different living things that they rely on to survive.

Ⓗ intrinsic brightness (of a star) A measure of the light that would reach a telescope if a star were at a standard distance from the Earth.

ion An electrically charged atom, or group of atoms.

ionising radiation Radiation with photons of sufficient energy to remove electrons from atoms in its path. Ionising radiation, such as ultraviolet, X-rays, and gamma rays, can damage living cells.

irradiation Being exposed to radiation from an external source.

joule A unit used to measure energy.

kidneys Organs in the body that removes waste urea from the blood, and balances water and blood plasma levels. People are usually born with two kidneys.

kilowatt-hour A unit used to measure energy. It is equivalent to using energy at a rate of 1 kilowatt for 1 hour. Power (kW) × time (hours).

landfill Disposing of rubbish in holes in the ground.

latitude The location of a place on Earth, north or south of the equator.

leach The movement of the plasticisers in a polymer into water, or another liquid, that is flowing past the polymer or is contained by it.

Leblanc process A process that used chalk (calcium carbonate), salt (sodium chloride) and coal to make the alkali, sodium carbonate. The Leblanc process was highly polluting.

lichen An organism consisting of a fungus growing with a simple photosynthetic organism called an alga. Lichens grow very slowly are often found growing on walls and roofs.

life cycle assessment A way of analysing the production, use, and disposal of a material or product to add up the total energy and water used and the effects on the environment.

lifestyle disease A disease that is not caused by microorganisms. They are triggered by other factors, for example, smoking, diet, and lack of exercise.

lifestyle The way in which people choose to live their lives, for example, what they choose to eat, how much exercise they choose to do, how much stress they experience in their job.

light pollution Light created by humans, for example, street lighting, that prevents city dwellers from seeing more than a few bright stars. It also causes problems for astronomers.

light-year The distance travelled by light in one year.

long-chain molecule Polymers are long-chain molecules. They consist of long chains of atoms.

longitudinal wave A wave in which the particles of the medium vibrate in the same direction as the wave is travelling. Sound is an example.

macroscopic Large enough to be seen without the help of a microscope.

magnetic A material that is attracted to a magnet. For example, iron is magnetic.

mantle A thick layer of rock beneath the Earth's crust, which extends about halfway down to the Earth's centre.

match Some studies into diseases compare two groups of people. People in each group are chosen to be as similar as possible (matched) so that the results can be fairly compared.

material The polymers, metals, glasses, and ceramics that we use to make all sorts of objects and structures.

mayfly larvae Mayflies spend most of their lives (up to three years) as larvae (also called mayfly nymphs). They live and feed in aquatic environments. The adult insects live on the wing for a short time, from a few hours to a few days.

mean value A type of average, found by adding up a set of measurements and then dividing by the number of measurements. You can have more confidence in the mean of a set of measurements than in a single measurement.

mechanism A process that explains why a particular factor causes an outcome.

medium (plural media) A material through which a wave travels.

melting point The temperature at which something melts.

memory cell A long-lived white blood cell, which is able to respond very quickly (by producing antibodies to destroy the microorganism) when it meets a microorganism for the second time.

metal Metals are materials with characteristic properties: they are shiny when polished and they conduct electricity.

metal The elements on the left side of the periodic table. Metals have characteristic properties: they are shiny when polished and they conduct electricity. Some metals react with acids to give salts and hydrogen. Metals are present as positive ions in salts.

microorganism A living organism that can only be seen through a microscope. They include bacteria, viruses, and fungi.

microwave radiation The radio wave with the highest frequency (shortest wavelength), used for mobile phones and satellite TV.

Milky Way The galaxy in which the Sun and its planets including Earth are located. It is seen from the Earth as an irregular, faintly luminous band across the night sky.

mixture Two or more different chemicals, mixed but not chemically joined together.

modulate To vary the amplitude or frequency of carrier waves so that they carry information.

molecule A group of atoms joined together. Most non-metals consist of molecules. Most compounds of non-metals with other non-metals are also molecular.

monoculture The continuous growing of one type of crop.

monomer A small molecule that can be joined to others like it in long chains to make a polymer.

mountain chain A group of mountains that extend along a line, often hundreds or even thousands of kilometres. Generally caused by the movement of tectonic plates.

mutation A change in the DNA of an organism. It alters a gene and may change the organism's characteristics.

nanometre A unit of length 1 000 000 000 times smaller than a metre. 1 nm = 0.001 μm = 0.000001 mm = 10^{-9} m.

nanoparticle A very tiny particle, whose size can be measured in nanometres.

nanotechnology The use and control of structures that are very small (1 to 100 nanometres in size)

National Grid A network of cables and transformers that connects power stations to the consumers who use the electricity.

natural A material that occurs naturally but may need processing to make it useful, such as silk, cotton, leather, iron ore, and bauxite.

natural polymer A polymer that occurs naturally but may need processing to make it useful, such as silk, cotton, leather, and asbestos.

natural selection When certain individuals are better suited to their environment they are more likely to survive and breed, passing on their features to the next generation.

ⓗ **negative feedback** A system where any change results in actions that reverse the original change.

neutralisation A reaction in which an acid reacts with an alkali to form a salt.

ⓗ **neutralisation** A reaction in which an acid reacts with an alkali to form a salt. During neutralisation reactions, the hydrogen ions in the acid solution react with hydroxide ions in the alkaline solution to make water molecules.

neutralise An acid will neutralise an alkali to form a salt. This is called a neutralisation reaction.

nitrogen cycle The continual cycling of nitrogen, which is one of the elements essential for life. By being converted to different chemical forms, nitrogen is able to pass between the atmosphere, lithosphere, hydrosphere, and biosphere.

ⓗ **nitrogen fixation** When nitrogen in the air is converted into nitrates in the soil by bacteria.

nitrogen-fixing bacteria Bacteria found in the soil and in swellings (nodules) on the roots of some plants (legumes), such as clover and peas. These bacteria take in nitrogen gas and make nitrates, which plants can absorb and use to make proteins.

noise Unwanted electrical signals that get added on to radio waves during transmission, causing additional modulation. Sometimes called 'interference'.

non-ionising radiation Radiation with photons that do not have enough energy to ionise molecules.

nuclear fuel In a nuclear reactor, a uranium atom splits and releases energy when hit by a neutron.

nucleus (plural nuclei) The central core of the atom. It is made up of protons and neutrons.

nucleus The central structure in a cell containing genetic material. It controls the function and characteristics of the cell.

observed brightness (of a star) A measure of the light reaching a telescope from a star.

oceanic ridge A line of underwater mountains in an ocean, where new seafloor constantly forms.

ⓗ **open-label trial** A clinical drug test in which both the patient and their doctor knows whether the patient is taking the new drug.

optical fibre A thin glass fibre, down which a light beam can travel. The beam is reflected at the sides so very little escapes. Used in modern communications, for example, to link computers in a building to a network.

organic matter Material that has come from dead plants and animals.

Glossary

outcome A variable that changes as a result of something else changing.

outlier A measured result that seems very different from other repeat measurements, or from the value you would expect, which you therefore strongly suspect is wrong.

oxidation A reaction that adds oxygen to a chemical.

ozone layer A thin layer in the atmosphere, about 30 km up, where oxygen is in the form of ozone molecules. The ozone layer absorbs ultraviolet radiation from sunlight.

parallax The apparent shift of an object against a more distant background, as the position of the observer changes. The further away an object is, the less it appears to shift. This can be used to measure how far away an object is, for example, to measure the distance to stars.

particulate A tiny bit of a solid.

passenger-kilometre A unit used to compare different transport systems to take account of how many passengers are carried. Number of passengers × distance travelled in km.

Ⓗ perceived risk The level of risk people that people think is attached to an activity, not based on data.

peer review The process whereby scientists who are experts in their field critically evaluate a scientific paper or idea before and after publication.

persistent organic pollutant (POP) A POP is an organic compound that does not break down in the environment for a very long time. POPs can spread widely around the world and build up in the fatty tissue of humans and animals. They can be harmful to people and the environment.

Ⓗ phenotype A description of the physical characteristics that an organism has (often related to a particular gene).

photon A tiny 'packet' of electromagnetic radiation. All electromagnetic waves are emitted and absorbed as photons. The energy of a photon is proportional to the frequency of the radiation.

photosynthesis A chemical reaction that happens in green plants using the energy in sunlight. The plant takes in water and carbon dioxide, and uses sunlight to convert them to glucose (a nutrient) and oxygen.

photovoltaic (PV) panel A device that uses the Sun's radiation to generate electricity.

phthalate A chemical that is used as a plasticiser, added to polymers to make them more flexible.

phytoplankton Single-celled photosynthetic organisms found in an ocean ecosystem.

Ⓗ pituitary gland The part of the human brain that coordinates many different functions, for example, release of ADH.

placebo Occasionally used in clinical trials, this looks like the drug being tested but contains no actual drug.

planet A very large, spherical object that orbits the Sun, or other star.

plasticiser A chemical (usually a small molecule) added to a polymer to make it more flexible.

pollutant Waste matter or chemical that contaminates the water, air, or soil.

polymer A material made of very long molecules formed by joining lots of small molecules, called monomers, together.

polymerise The joining together of lots of small molecules called monomers to form a long-chain molecule called a polymer.

population A group of animals or plants of the same species living in the same area.

potential difference (p.d.) The difference in potential energy (for each unit of charge flowing) between any two points in an electric circuit.

power In an electric circuit, the rate at which work is done by the battery or power supply on the components in a circuit. Power is equal to current × voltage.

predator An animal that kills other animals (its prey) for food.

Ⓗ pre-implantation genetic diagnosis (PGD) This is the technical term for embryo selection. Embryos fertilised outside the body are tested for genetic disorders. Only healthy embryos are put into the mother's uterus.

primary energy source A source of energy not derived from any other energy source, for example, fossil fuels or uranium.

principal frequency The frequency that is emitted with the highest intensity.

processing centre The part of a control system that receives and processes information from the receptor, and triggers action by the effectors.

producer The organism found at the start of a food chain. Producers are able to make their own food.

product A new chemical formed during a chemical reaction.

properties The physical or chemical characteristics of a chemical. The properties of a chemical are what make it different from other chemicals.

proportional Two variables are proportional if there is a constant ratio between them.

protein Chemicals in living things that are polymers made by joining together amino acids.

pulse rate The rate at which the heart beats. The pulse is measured by pressing on an artery in the neck, wrist, or groin.

P-wave A seismic wave through the Earth, produced during an earthquake.

Ⓗ P-wave A longitudinal seismic wave through the Earth, produced during an earthquake.

radiation A flow of energy from a source. Light and infrared are examples. Radiation spreads out from its source, and may be absorbed or reflected by objects in its path. It may also go (be transmitted) through them.

radio wave Electromagnetic wave of a much lower frequency than visible light. Radio waves can be made to carry signals and are widely used for communications.

radioactive Used to describe a material, atom, or element that produces ionising radiation.

random Of no predictable pattern.

range The difference between the highest and the lowest of a set of measurements.

reactant A chemical on the left-hand side of an equation. These chemicals react to form the products.

Ⓗ real difference One way of deciding if there is a real difference between two values is to look at the mean values and the ranges. The difference between two mean values is real if their ranges do not overlap.

receptor The part of a control system that detects changes in the system and passes this information to the processing centre.

recessive An allele that will only show up in an organism when a dominant allele of the gene is not present. You must have two copies of a recessive allele to have the feature it produces.

recycling A range of methods for making new materials from materials that have already been used.

redshift When radiation is observed to have longer wavelengths than expected. (Red light has the longest wavelength of visible light.)

reduction A reaction that removes oxygen from a chemical.

regulation A rule that can be enforced by an authority, for example, the government. The law that says that all vehicles that are three years old and older must have an annual exhaust emission test is a regulation that helps to reduce atmospheric pollution.

renewable energy source A resource that can be used to generate electricity without being used up, such as the wind, tides, and sunlight.

repeatable A quality of a measurement that gives the same result when repeated under the same conditions.

reproducible A quality of a measurement that gives the same result when carried out under different conditions, for example, by different people or using different equipment or methods.

reproduction The production of offspring through a sexual or asexual process.

reproductive isolation Two populations are reproductively isolated if they are unable to breed with each other.

respiration A series of chemical reactions in cells that release energy for the cell to use.

risk factor A variable linked to an increased risk of disease. Risk factors are linked to disease but may not be the cause of the disease.

risk The probability of an outcome that is seen as undesirable, associated with some behaviour or process.

rock cycle Continuing changes in rock material, caused by processes such as erosion, sedimentation, compression, and heating.

rubber A material that is easily stretched or bent. Natural rubber is a natural polymer obtained from latex, the sap of a rubber tree.

salt A compound formed when an acid neutralises an alkali.

Sankey diagram A flow diagram used to show what happens to energy during a process. The width of the arrows are proportional to the energy flow.

seafloor spreading The process of forming new ocean floor at oceanic ridges.

secondary energy source Energy in a form that can be distributed easily but is manufactured by using a raw energy resource such as a fossil fuel or wind. Examples of secondary energy sources are electricity, hot water used in heating systems, and steam.

sedimentary rock Rock formed from layers of sediment.

seismic wave A wave produced by the vibrations caused by an earthquake.

selective absorption Some materials absorb some forms of electromagnetic radiation but not others. For example, glass absorbs some infrared but is transparent to visible light.

selective breeding Choosing parent organisms with certain characteristics and mating them to try to produce offspring that have these characteristics.

sensitivity The ability to detect small changes, for example, radiation or temperature.

sex cells Cells produced by males and females for reproduction – sperm cells and egg cells. Sex cells carry a copy of the parent's genetic information. They join together at fertilisation.

sexual reproduction Reproduction where the sex cells from two individuals fuse together to form an embryo.

shielding Materials used to absorb radiation.

signal Information carried through a communication system, for example, by an electromagnetic wave with variations in its amplitude or frequency, or being rapidly switched on and off.

social context The situation of people's lives.

soft A material that is easy to dent or scratch.

solar power Power supplied by electromagnetic radiation from the Sun.

Solar System The Sun and objects that orbit around it – planets and their moons, comets, and asteroids.

solution Formed when a solid, liquid, or gas dissolves in a solvent.

source An object that produces radiation.

species A group of organisms that can breed to produce fertile offspring.

spectrum One example is the continuous band of colours, from violet to red, produced by shining white light through a prism. Passing light from a flame test through a prism produces a line spectrum.

speed of light 300 000 kilometres per second – the speed of all electromagnetic waves in a vacuum.

stem cell An unspecialised animal cell that can divide and develop into a specialised cell.

stiff A material that is difficult to bend or stretch.

strong A material that is hard to pull apart or crush.

structural Making up the structure (of a cell or organism).

structural protein A protein that is used to build cells.

subsidence The sinking of the ground's surface when it collapses into a hole beneath it.

Sun The star nearest Earth. Fusion of hydrogen in the Sun releases energy, which makes life on Earth possible.

surface area How much exposed surface a solid object has.

sustainability Using resources and the environment to meet the needs of people today without damaging Earth or reducing the resources for people in the future.

sustainable Meeting the needs of today without damaging the Earth for future generations.

S-wave A seismic wave through the Earth, produced during an earthquake.

Ⓗ S-wave A transverse seismic wave through the Earth, produced during an earthquake.

symptom What a person has when they have a particular illness, for example, a rash, high temperature, or sore throat.

synthetic A material made by a chemical process, not naturally occurring.

tectonic plates Giant slabs of rock (about 12, comprising crust and upper mantle) that make up the Earth's outer layer.

telescope An instrument that gathers electromagnetic radiation to form an image or to map data, from astronomical objects such as stars and galaxies. It makes visible things that cannot be seen with the naked eye.

Glossary

tension A material is in tension when forces are trying to stretch it or pull it apart.

termination When medicine or surgical treatment is used to end a pregnancy.

theory A scientific explanation that is generally accepted by the scientific community.

thermal panel A device that uses the Sun's radiation to heat water.

thermal power station A power station that heats water to produce steam to drive turbines.

tidal power station A power station that uses the tides to drive turbines to generate electricity.

toxic A chemical that may lead to serious health risks, or even death, if breathed in, swallowed, or taken in through the skin.

transformer An electrical device, consisting of two coils of wire wound on an iron core. An alternating current in one coil causes an everchanging magnetic field that induces an alternating current in the other. Used to 'step' voltage up or down to the level required.

transmitted (transmit) When radiation hits an object, it may go through it. It is said to be transmitted through it. We also say that a radio aerial transmits a signal. In this case, transmits means 'emits' or 'sends out'.

transverse wave A wave in which the particles of the medium vibrate at right angles to the direction in which the wave is travelling. Water waves are an example.

turbine A device that is made to spin by a flow of air, water, or steam. It is used to drive a generator.

ultraviolet radiation (UV) Electromagnetic waves with frequencies higher than those of visible light, beyond the violet end of the visible spectrum.

uncertain Describes measurements where scientists know that they may not have recorded the true value.

uncertainty The amount by which a measurement could differ from the true value.

Universe All things (including the Earth and everything else in space).

unspecialised A cell that has not yet developed into one particular type of cell.

vaccination Introducing to the body a chemical (a vaccine) used to make a person immune to a disease. A vaccine contains weakened or dead microorganisms, or parts of the microorganism, so that the body makes antibodies to the disease without being ill.

variation Differences between living organisms. This could be differences between species. There are also differences between members of a population from the same species.

vein A blood vessel that carries blood towards the heart.

vibrate To move rapidly and repeatedly back and forth.

virus A microorganism that can only live and reproduce inside living cells.

volcano A vent in the Earth's surface that erupts magma, gases, and solids.

voltage The voltage marked on a battery or power supply is a measure of the 'push' it exerts on charges in an electric circuit. The 'voltage' between two points in a circuit means the 'potential difference' between these points.

vulcanisation A process for hardening natural rubber by making crosslinks between the polymer molecules.

watt The unit used to measure power: 1 watt = 1 joule/second.

wave power Using the sea waves to drive turbines to generate electricity.

wave speed The speed at which waves move through a medium.

wavelength The distance between one wave crest (or wave trough) and the next.

H **wet scrubbing** A process used to remove pollutants from flue gases.

white blood cell A cell in the blood that fights microorganisms. Some white blood cells digest invading microorganisms. Others produce antibodies.

wind farm A power station that uses the wind to drive turbines to generate electricity.

word equation A summary in words of a chemical reaction.

X-ray Electromagnetic waves with high frequency, well above that of visible light.

XX chromosomes The pair of sex chromosomes found in a human female's body cells.

XY chromosomes The pair of sex chromosomes found in a human male's body cells.

Answers

B1 Workout

1
a Cell **b** Genes **c** Nucleus **d** Chromosome **e** DNA

2 Dimples – one gene only
Weight – genes and environment
Eye colour – several genes working together
Scars – environment only

3 **a** T **b** T **c** F
d F **e** F

4 Unspecialised, asexual, clones, environments

5 **a** If the test is positive, should I have an abortion?
b If the test is positive, should I father a child?

6 **a**

	R	r
R	RR	Rr
r	Rr	rr

b **i** 75%
ii 25%

7 –

B1 Quickfire

1 Chromosomes, genes, instructions, proteins, DNA

2 True statements: **a**, **b**
Corrected versions of false statements:
c If a person has one dominant allele in a pair of alleles, they will show the characteristic linked to that gene.
d Human male body cells have XY sex chromosomes.
e A sperm contains chromosomes that are not paired up.

3 Thick mucus, difficulty breathing, chest infections, digestion problems

4 Is the father a carrier of cystic fibrosis? Would she consider having a termination if the fetus had cystic fibrosis? Is she prepared for the increased risk of miscarriage when cells are removed from the fetus for testing?

5 **a** Ellie, Susan and Tom
b

Ellie / Jim

	M	m
m	Mm	mm
m	Mm	mm

The chance their baby has Marfan syndrome is 50%.

6 **a** Rr **b** 2, 6, 7, 10 **c** 3, 4, 5, 8, 9, 11

7 Tremor, clumsiness, memory loss, inability to concentrate, mood changes

8 A stem cell is an unspecialised cell. Embryonic stem cells are extracted from embryos. They can develop into any type of cell. Adult stem cells can develop into many, but not all, types of cells.

9 **a** A person's genotype describes a person's genes. So the genotype of people represented by those on the top line is XX. The phenotype describes the characteristics of a living organism. The phenotype of those on the top line is that they are female.

b Two offspring genotypes are XX (phenotype female) and two genotypes are XY (phenotype male). So there is a 50% chance of a baby being female.

10 **a** She has dimples.
b Dominant – she has dimples even though she has only one **D** allele.
c Heterozygous – she has two different versions of the dimple allele.

11 The Y chromosome includes a sex-determining gene. This makes an embryo develop testes, and so become male. When there is no Y chromosome, the embryo develops ovaries. It is female.

12 **a** Pre-implantation genetic diagnosis involves creating embryos outside the body, and testing them for an inherited disorder. An embryo that will not develop the inherited disorder is selected for implantation into the uterus
b If a man and a woman are carriers of a genetic disease
c Whether they would be prepared to abort a fetus with the genetic disease; whether removing a cell to test damages an embryo

13 Scientists remove an egg cell nucleus. They take a nucleus from an adult body cell of the organism they want to clone, and transfer it to the 'empty' egg cell. They grow the embryo for a few days and implant it into a uterus.

B1 GCSE-style questions

1 **a** **i** They have the same combination of alleles; they both developed from one egg that was fertilised by one sperm;
ii Their cells certain 23 pairs of chromosomes.
iii XX

b **i** They have different lifestyles.
ii A stem cell is an unspecialised cell.
iii To treat diseases

2 **a** **i** 50%
ii 2
b **i**

Sarah / Alan

	T	t
t	Tt	tt
t	Tt	tt

ii 50%

3 **a** Two from: tremor, clumsiness, memory loss, inability to concentrate, mood changes
b Abigail and Brenda
c For the test: they can consider having a termination if the test is positive. Against the test: deciding whether or not to have a termination is a very difficult decision.

4 5/6 marks
Answer clearly explains why siblings show variation **and** explains why children have different characteristics from their parents.
All information in the answer is relevant, clear, organised and presented in a structured and coherent format.
Specialist terms are used appropriately. Few, if any, errors in grammar, punctuation and spelling.

3/4 marks

Answer explains clearly **either** why siblings show variation

or why children have different characteristics from their parents.

OR explains each point above but lacks detail/clarity. Most of the information is relevant and presented in a structured and coherent format. Specialist terms are usually used correctly. There are occasional errors in grammar, punctuation and spelling.

1/2 marks

Answer explains **either** why siblings show variation

or why children have different characteristics from their parents.

AND the explanation lacks detail/clarity.

There may be limited use of specialist terms. Errors of grammar, punctuation and spelling prevent communication of the science. Answer includes 1 or 2 points of those listed below.

0 marks

Insufficient or irrelevant science. Answer not worthy of credit.

Relevant points include:

- Children inherit alleles from both parents
- There are two possible types of allele for each gene
- A child inherits alleles when a sex cell (sperm) from his or her dad fertilizes a sex cell (egg) from his or her mum
- The sex cells contained one version of each allele from each parent – this explains why children have different characteristics from their parents
- Alleles pair up on fertilization, so body cells contain pairs of alleles
- The combinations of alleles in each pair determine the characteristics of a child
- Different children in a family (except identical twins) inherit different combinations of alleles from their parents – this is why siblings show variation

5 a A child can get the disease even if their parents did not have the disease.
   b Rod, Barbara, Sally, Philip
   c Mitch and Tracy
   d Phenotype describes the observable characteristics of the person, including unsteady walking, slurring of speech, and reduced appetite. Genotype describes the combination of alleles an organism has. A person with Niemann-Pick disorder has two copies of the faulty gene. The alleles from both parents are identical.
   e i   Pre-implantation genetic diagnosis involves removing one cell from each of several embryos made outside the body. The cells are then tested for faulty alleles. An embryo without faulty alleles is chosen for implantation in the uterus.
      ii Implications include: the possibility that removing a cell to test damages the embryo; the ethical question of whether it is right to destroy embryos with faulty alleles; the possibility of tests providing false positive or false negative results.

C1 Workout

1 78% nitrogen; 21% oxygen; 1% argon

2 The early atmosphere was mainly **carbon dioxide** and **water vapour**.
   Water vapour **condensed** to form oceans. Carbon dioxide **dissolved** in the oceans. Later it formed **sedimentary** rocks. Early plants removed **carbon dioxide** from the atmosphere by photosynthesis, and added **oxygen** to the atmosphere.

3 Car A, going into engine: N_2, O_2; coming out of exhaust: CO_2, H_2O, N_2
   Car B, going into engine: N_2, O_2; coming out of exhaust: CO_2, H_2O, N_2, NO, NO_2, C, CO

4 Carbon or hydrogen; hydrogen or carbon; oxygen; carbon dioxide; water; chemical or combustion or burning; number; products; rearranged; products; products

5

	Reactants		Products
Name	coal (with no sulfur impurities)	oxygen (from a plentiful supply of air)	carbon dioxide
Formula	C	O_2	CO_2
Diagram			

	Reactants		Product		
Name	coal (with no sulfur impurities)	oxygen (from a limited supply of air)	carbon dioxide	carbon monoxide	particulate carbon
Formula	C	O_2	CO_2	CO	C
Diagram					

	Reactants		Products	
Name	coal (with sulfur impurities)	oxygen (from a plentiful supply of air)	carbon dioxide	sulfur dioxide
Formula	C and S	O_2	CO_2	SO_2
Diagram				

6 Suggested answers include:
   We should replace diesel and petrol with biofuels because the plants from which biofuels are made remove carbon dioxide from the atmosphere.
   No we shouldn't. The problem with biofuels is that they produce carbon dioxide when they burn.
   I think electric vehicles are better because they produce no pollutants as they travel.
   True, but there are problems with electric vehicles. One is that the electricity may have been generated by burning fossil fuels.

7

Pollutant name	Pollutant formula	Where the pollutant comes from	Problems the pollutant causes	One way of reducing the amount of this pollutant added to the atmosphere
sulfur dioxide	SO_2	burning fossil fuels with sulfur impurities	acid rain	remove sulfur impurities from fuels before burning
nitrogen oxides	NO_2 NO	burning fuels in car engines	acid rain asthma	fit catalytic converters to cars
carbon dioxide	CO_2	burning fossil fuels	global warming	burn less fossil fuels
carbon monoxide	CO	burning fossil fuels in a limited supply of oxygen	poisoning	make sure oxygen supply is plentiful
particulate carbon	C	burning fossil fuels in a limited supply of oxygen	makes surfaces dirty	make sure oxygen supply is plentiful

C1 Quickfire

1 Sulfur dioxide – acid rain
Carbon dioxide – climate change
Carbon monoxide – reduces the amount of oxygen the blood carries
Particulate carbon – makes surfaces dirty

2 Argon – 1%; nitrogen – 78%; oxygen – 21%

3 Carbon, hydrocarbons, hydrogen, oxygen, carbon dioxide

4 True: **a, d, e**
Corrected versions of false sentences:
b The spaces between molecules in the air are large.
c Carbon monoxide is directly harmful to humans.

5 C, B, D, A

6 Carbon dioxide dissolved in the oceans, and some of its carbon atoms ended up in sedimentary rocks. Early plants used carbon dioxide for photosynthesis.

7 Hydrocarbon, oxygen, oxidation, reduction

8

Formula	Diagram of molecule	Name
CO		carbon monoxide
SO_2		sulfur dioxide
CO_2		carbon dioxide
NO_2		nitrogen dioxide
H_2O		water
NO		nitrogen monoxide

9 Have more efficient engines that burn less fuel; use low-sulfur fuels; use catalytic converters; use more public transport; have and enforce legal limits on exhaust emissions

10 The same total number of atoms of each element are present in both the reactants and products; the atoms are rearranged in the reaction.

11 Nitrogen, nitrogen monoxide, NO, nitrogen dioxide, NO_2, NO_x, acid rain

12 Spray seawater at the flue gases. Substances in the seawater react with sulfur dioxide. Allow the flue gases to be in contact with a slurry of calcium sulfate and water. Sulfur dioxide and calcium sulfate react to make calcium sulfate.

13 Benefits: the plants from which biofuels are made remove carbon dioxide from the atmosphere; renewable. Problems: add carbon dioxide to the atmosphere on burning; may be grown on land that could be used for food crops.

14 Electric cars produce no air pollutants at point of use, unlike diesel cars. However, the electricity might have been generated by burning fossil fuels. Electric cars need to be recharged more frequently than diesel cars need to be refuelled.

15 11 g

16 32 g

17 2 g

18 9 g

C1 GCSE-style questions

1 a

	Run 1	Run 2	Run 3	Run 4
Volume of air in syringes at start (cm³)	100	100	100	100
Volume of air in syringes at end (cm³)	82	86	**85**	84
Decrease in volume (cm³)	18	**14**	15	16

b 15.75 cm³
c The percentage of oxygen in the air is 21%, so the volume of oxygen in 100 cm³ air is 21 cm³. You would expect the copper to react with all the oxygen in the syringes.
d Some of the oxygen in the syringes did not react with the copper **or** there was not enough copper to react with all the oxygen from the air.

2 a i +

ii Hydrocarbon fuels with sulfur impurities
b i Increased
ii More coal-fired power stations or more vehicles burning hydrocarbon fuels or any other sensible answer
c i Nitrogen; oxygen
ii Acid rain damages buildings made of limestone; acid rain makes lakes more acidic; acid rain damages trees.
d Sulfur dioxide gas emissions decreased between 1980 and 2000.

Answers

3 5/6 marks

Answer clearly describes the correlation shown by the data in the table

and gives examples to illustrate the trend

and points out one or more exceptions to the overall trend, giving an example

and states and explains why it is not possible to say whether increased mass causes increased emissions

All information in the answer is relevant, clear, organised and presented in a structured and coherent format. Specialist terms are used appropriately. Few, if any, errors in grammar, punctuation and spelling.

3/4 marks

Answer describes the correlation shown by the data in the table, but does not give examples to illustrate the trend

and points out one or more exceptions to the overall trend

or states that it is not possible to say whether increased mass causes increased emissions

Most of the information is relevant and presented in a structured and coherent format. Specialist terms are usually used correctly. There are occasional errors in grammar, punctuation and spelling.

1/2 marks

Answer describes the correlation shown by the data in the table, but does not give examples to illustrate the trend

and does not point out exceptions to the overall trend

or states that it is not possible to say whether increased mass causes increased emissions

There may be limited use of specialist terms. Errors of grammar, punctuation and spelling prevent communication of the science. Answer includes 1 or 2 points of those listed below.

0 marks

Insufficient or irrelevant science. Answer not worthy of credit.

Relevant points include:

- Overall, there is a correlation between the car mass and average CO_2 emissions – the heavier the car, the greater the mass of average CO_2 emissions...
- ... for example the Fox has a mass of 978 kg and emissions of 144 g/km, and the car with the greatest mass (the Toureg, 2214 kg) has emissions of 324 g/km.
- Not all the data fits the pattern exactly...
- ...for example the Fox has a mass of 978 kg and emissions of 144 g/km, and the Polo has a mass that is greater than the Fox (1000 kg) but smaller emissions of 138 g/km.
- It is not possible to say whether the increased mass causes increased emissions...
- ...because the increased emissions could be caused by some other factor.

P1 Workout

1 **a** C   **b** A   **c** D   **d** A

2 **a** 12 700   **b** Four thousand million
  c 10   **d** Five thousand million
  e 14 thousand million

3 G, F, E, A, H, I, D, B, C

4 **a** Comet: big lump of ice and dust that rushes past the Sun and then returns to the outer Solar System; asteroid: lump of rock that is usually smaller than a comet, with an almost circular orbit.

b Moon: orbits a planet, and is smaller than the planet it orbits; planet: orbits the Sun and is bigger than its moons.

c Star: ball of hot gas; galaxy: made up of thousands of millions of stars.

5 Vibrations at right angles – transverse – S-waves and water waves

Vibrations in same direction – longitudinal – P-waves and sound waves

6

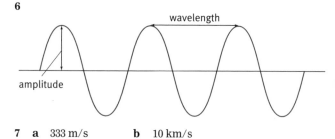

7 **a** 333 m/s   **b** 10 km/s

P1 Quickfire

1 Moving out from the centre: core, mantle, crust

2 Objects that emit light: **b, c**

3 Brightness, pollution, uncertainties, assumptions.

4 **a** A travelling vibration that transfers energy from place to place without transferring matter
  b The number of waves that pass any point each second
  c The distance between two corresponding points on adjacent cycles
  d The distance from the maximum displacement to the undisturbed position
  e The distance light travels through a vacuum in one year

5 **a** 2050 km   **b** 2050 km   **c** 20 400 m

6 C, A, D, B, E

7 Shapes of continents seem to fit together; matching fossils in eastern South America and western Africa; matching rock types in eastern South America and western Africa

8 Wegener was an outsider to the community of geologists; the movement of the continents was not detectable with the measuring instruments of the time; the idea seemed too big from the limited evidence available.

9 **a** 7.5 km/s   **b** 9 km/s

10 **a** About 2060 km
  b The speed of the S-waves is 0 between a depth of about 2060 km and 5000 km. This is evidence that the material that makes up the outer core is liquid, since S-waves cannot travel through liquids.

11 **a** Redshift – the shifting of light emitted by distant galaxies towards the red end of the spectrum – is evidence for distant galaxies moving away from us.
  b Galaxies that are further away from us moving faster than those that are closer is evidence that space is expanding.
  c The pattern of stripes in the rocks formed at oceanic ridges is evidence that the Earth's magnetic field has changed direction several times in the past.

12 See the diagram of the rock cycle in the Factbank.

P1 GCSE-style questions

1 a Galileo saw Ganymede through a telescope.
Gan Dej saw an object close to Jupiter with a telescope.
Ganymede is a moon.

b When Gan Dej made his observations, the skies would have been very dark. The apparent magnitude of Ganymede is smaller than that of the faintest object in Space that can be seen in a very dark sky without a telescope, so it is possible for Gan Dej to have seen Ganymede.

c i Ganymede orbits a planet, not a star.
ii The mass of Pluto is less than the total mass of the other objects that cross its orbit.
iii Xena orbits the Sun.

2 a From centre: core, mantle, crust   b 1C; 2D; 3B; 4A

3 a P-waves travel faster. They arrive at the seismometer first.

b i

seismograph	S-P time interval (s)
A	approximately 52
B	approximately 74
C	approximately 20

ii Seismograph C was recorded closest to the earthquake. The S-P interval is smallest.

c i Distance = speed × time
Distance = 5 km/s × 60 s
Distance = 300 km
ii Owlton and Badgerbridge

B2 Workout

1 Top empty box: reproduce rapidly
Empty boxes on middle line: make toxins and damage cells
Bottom empty box: disease symptoms

2 a Experts meet every April...
b The eggs provide food...
c Technicians break...
d This flu virus is delivered...

3 2C, 3D, 4K, 5E, 6F, 8G, 9H, 10L, 11I, 12J

B2 Quickfire

1 b, c

2 a G   b L   c L
d L   e L   f G

3 Pulse rate – number of heart beats per minute
Lower blood pressure measurement – pressure against artery wall when heart is relaxed
Higher blood pressure measurement – pressure against artery wall when heart is contracting

4 True statements: b, c, e
Corrected versions of false statements:
a Antibiotics kill bacteria.
d In clinical trials, new drugs are tested for effectiveness on people with the illness.

5

Part of circulation system	What does it do?	What is it made from?
heart	pumps blood around the body	muscle
artery	takes blood from your heart to the rest of your body	thick walls made from muscle and elastic fibres
vein	brings blood back to your heart from the rest of your body	thin walls made of muscle and elastic fibres
capillary	takes blood to and from tissues, and allows oxygen and food to diffuse into cells and waste to diffuse out of cells	very thin walls (one cell thick)

6 A, C, F, D, E, G, B

7 Receptor – detects changes in the environment
Processing centre – receives information and processes responses
Effector – produces the response

8 Vaccines and medicines may have unwanted side-effects.

9 Complete the whole course of treatment; only take antibiotics when necessary.

10 a Neither P nor D   b P   c D, P

11 Long-term human trials for new drugs ensure that the drugs are safe, and that they work. The trials may also identify side-effects that do not occur immediately.

12 Antimicrobial resistance develops when random changes in bacteria or fungi genes make new varieties that the antimicrobial cannot kill or inhibit.

13 Temperature sensor – receptors in brain; thermostat system with switch – pituitary gland; heater – ADH and kidneys

14 Alcohol suppresses ADH, which leads to the production of a greater volume of more dilute urine. Ecstasy leads to increased ADH production, which results in a smaller volume of more concentrated urine.

B2 GCSE-style questions

1 a i Reproduction
ii 4
b i White
ii Taking anti-diarrhoea tablets would mean that *Salmonella* bacteria would stay in the intestines for longer.

2 a Increased, opinion B *or* C *or* D, decreased, opinion A
b A, E, G, C, F, B, D

3 5/6 marks
Answer clearly explains why **AND** how water levels in the cells of a human body are kept constant
and explains how alcohol and Ecstasy affect the amount and concentration of urine.
All information in the answer is relevant, clear, organised and presented in a structured and coherent format.
Specialist terms are used appropriately. Few, if any, errors in grammar, punctuation and spelling.

3/4 marks
Answer clearly explains why **AND** how water levels in the cells of a human body are kept constant
OR explains how alcohol and Ecstasy affect the amount and concentration of urine.
OR explains each point above but lacks detail/clarity.
Most of the information is relevant and presented in a structured and coherent format. Specialist terms are usually used correctly. There are occasional errors in grammar, punctuation and spelling.

1/2 marks
Answer clearly explains why **OR** how water levels in the cells of a human body are kept constant
OR explains how alcohol and Ecstasy affect the amount and concentration of urine.
AND the explanation lacks detail/clarity.
There may be limited use of specialist terms. Errors of grammar, punctuation and spelling prevent communication of the science. Answer includes 1 or 2 points of those listed below.

0 marks
Insufficient or irrelevant science. Answer not worthy of credit.
Relevant points include:
- Cells only work properly if the concentrations of their contents are correct. So their water levels must be kept constant.
- Kidneys control water levels in the body by responding to changes in water levels in blood plasma.
- Water levels in blood plasma may decrease because of sweating, eating salty food, not drinking much water.
- When water levels in blood plasma are low, kidneys make smaller quantities of concentrated urine.
- When water levels in blood plasma are high, kidneys make bigger quantities of dilute urine.
- Alcohol leads to big volumes of dilute urine.
- Ecstasy leads to small volumes of concentrated urine.

4   **5/6 marks**
Answer clearly explains how a negative feedback system keeps water levels constant in the cells of a human body **and** includes the names of the hormones and organs involved in the system
All information in the answer is relevant, clear, organised and presented in a structured and coherent format. Specialist terms are used appropriately. Few, if any, errors in grammar, punctuation and spelling.

3/4 marks
Answer explains how a negative feedback system keeps water levels constant in the cells of a human body
OR states the names of the hormones and organs involved in the system
OR explains each point above but lacks detail/clarity.
Most of the information is relevant and presented in a structured and coherent format. Specialist terms are usually used correctly. There are occasional errors in grammar, punctuation and spelling.

1/2 marks
Answer explains how a negative feedback system keeps water levels constant in the cells of a human body
OR states the names of the hormones and organs involved in the system

AND the explanation lacks detail/clarity.
There may be limited use of specialist terms. Errors of grammar, punctuation and spelling prevent communication of the science. Answer includes 1 or 2 points of those listed below.

0 marks
Insufficient or irrelevant science. Answer not worthy of credit.
Relevant points include:
- Receptors in the brain detect changes in concentration of blood plasma.
- If the concentration is too high, the pituitary gland releases ADH – a hormone – into the blood stream
- The ADH travels to the kidneys – (the effectors.)
- The more ADH that arrives, the more water the kidneys reabsorb in the body..
- ...and the more concentrated the urine.
- If smaller amounts of ADH arrive at the kidneys, large quantities of dilute urine are made.

C2 Workout

1   Example answers are given here – many others are possible.

Part of tricycle	Properties this part of the tricycle must have	Material
tyres	high frictional forces with ground	rubber
brake	high frictional force with wheel	plastic
frame	high strength	steel
seat	high strength, not cold to the touch	polypropene
handle to push tricycle	high strength, not cold to the touch	polypropene
pushing pole	high strength	aluminium
screws that join pushing pole to handle	resistant to corrosion	stainless steel
bag	flexible	polythene

2

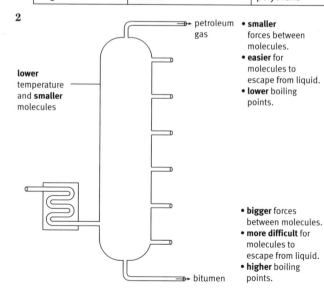

petroleum gas
- **smaller** forces between molecules.
- **easier** for molecules to escape from liquid.
- **lower** boiling points.

lower temperature and **smaller** molecules

- **bigger** forces between molecules.
- **more difficult** for molecules to escape from liquid.
- **higher** boiling points.

bitumen

3

Observation	Suggested reason
Nano-sized particles get into the nuclei of cancer cells more easily than normal-sized gold particles.	Gold nano-particles are much smaller than normal gold particles.

Action	Suggested reason
The scientists tried to stop cancer cells dividing.	They knew this would kill the cancer cells.
The scientists did the tests on cancer cells outside the body.	They did not want to risk harming the patients. It might not have been considered ethical to do the tests on people.
The scientists took cancer cells from many people.	To check that the gold nanoparticles killed cancerous cells from many people, not just from one person.
In future, when the scientists do tests on cancer cells inside the body, they will try to prevent gold nanoparticles entering the nuclei healthy cells.	If gold enters the nucleus of a cell, it is likely to kill the cell, whether or not it is cancerous.

4   Top diagram – make cross-links between polymer chains – harder, stronger, less flexible; second from top diagram – pack molecules neatly together with crystalline regions – stronger, denser; second from bottom diagram – increase chain length – stronger; bottom diagram – add plasticizer – softer, more flexible.

5   **a** C   **b** P   **c** C   **d** P

6   **a** One more oxygen molecule
   b Two more carbon dioxide molecules
   c Three more water molecules

C2 Quickfire

1   **a, d, e, f**

2   True statement: **c**
Corrected versions of false statements:
a A synthetic material is one which is made from non-living materials.
b A hydrocarbon is a compound made of carbon and hydrogen only.
d Monomers are small molecules that join together to form polymers.
e Most crude oil is used to make fuels.
f In a chemical reaction, there are always the same number of atoms of each element in the products and in the reactants.

3   Molecules, 1, 100, nm, fuel combustion products, seaspray.

4   The dental polymer matches the colour of teeth, it has no know health risks and is a poor conductor of heat, meaning it does not cause pain when very cold or very hot food and drink are consumed.

5   Polypropene is stronger under tension and does not rot.

6   HDPE is stronger and stiffer.

7   Fractions, greater, higher, lower down.

8   Nanoparticles have a much larger surface area compared to their volume.

9   Silver nanoparticles are added to fibres (in wound dressings and socks, for example) to give antibacterial properties. Nanoparticles are also added to plastics for sports equipment to make them stronger.

10   Nanoparticles may have harmful effects on health. Some people think they should not be widely used until these effects have been fully investigated.

11   **a** Increased chain length increases strength since longer molecules become more tangled and so more difficult to separate.
   b Cross-linking increases hardness and strength, and decreases flexibility. This is because cross-linking holds the polymer chains together in a rigid pattern.
   c Adding a plasticiser makes a polymer softer and more flexible. This is because the molecules of plasticiser hold the polymer chains apart.
   d Increasing crystallinity increases strength and density because the forces between the molecules are slightly stronger, so more energy is needed to separate them.

C2 GCSE-style questions

1   **a** Artificial heart valves D, hospital laundry bags C, fillings for front teeth B, contact lenses A
   b **i** Cellulose
      ii Non-toxic, flexible, high strength in tension
     iii Polymerisation

2   **a** Density values: aluminium alloy = 2.65 g/cm³; ABS steel = 7.10 g/cm³; glass reinforced plastic = 1.40 g/cm³
   b Points that may be included:
- Glass reinforced plastic (GRP) and the aluminium alloy have lower densities than ABS steel, so boats of a given size made from GRP and the aluminium alloy will be lighter than a boat of the same size made of ABS steel
- A boat made from GRP is much more likely to shatter on impact with rocks than one made from the aluminium alloy or the ABS steel
- The aluminium alloy and ABS steel are stronger than GRP
- A reasoned choice of material

3   5/6 marks
Answer clearly identifies all the advantages **and** disadvantages of the three materials in the table as building materials, referring to data in the table, **and** comes to a judgement about which is the best material from which to build a house **and** gives clear reasons for the judgement.
All information in the answer is relevant, clear, organised, and presented in a structured and coherent format. Specialist terms are used appropriately. Few, if any, errors in grammar, punctuation, and spelling.

3/4 marks
Answer identifies some advantages **and** disadvantages of the three materials in the table as building materials, in some cases referring to data in the table
and gives to a judgement about which is the best material from which to build a house.
Most of the information is relevant and presented in a structured and coherent format. Specialist terms are usually used correctly. There are occasional errors in grammar, punctuation and spelling.

Answers

1/2 marks

Answer identifies a few advantages **or** disadvantages of some of the materials in the table as building materials, but does not refer to data in the table

or identifies a few advantages **and** disadvantages of one of the materials in the table as a building material, but does not refer to data in the table

or gives a judgement about which material is the best material from which to build a house.

There may be limited use of specialist terms. Errors of grammar, punctuation and spelling prevent communication of the science. Answer includes 1 or 2 points of those listed below.

0 marks

Insufficient or irrelevant science. Answer not worthy of credit.

Relevant points include:
- The compressive strength values for limestone and concrete are the same, at 60 MPa.
- The compressive strength of wood (15 MPa) is much less than that of limestone and concrete (60 MPa)
- Considering strength alone, limestone and concrete are better building materials than wood
- The thermal conductivity of wood (0.1 W/mK) is much less than that of limestone (1.3 W/mK) and concrete (1.7 W/mK)...
- ...This means that wood is a better insulator, and so a house made from wood would lose heat less quickly than an identical house made from limestone or concrete
- A reasoned decision about which material is best, taking into account all the factors above

4 a The forces between long hydrocarbon molecules are stronger than the forces between short hydrocarbon molecules; the stronger the forces between molecules, the more energy is needed to separate them.

b i Shower curtains, because they need to be most flexible

ii The rubber in car tyres, because it needs to be more rigid, harder and stronger.

P2 Workout

1 The satellite both absorbs and emits radiation. The air transmits radiation. The transmitter is a source of radiation. The satellite dish is a detector. It absorbs radiation. The energy deposited here by a beam of radiation depends on the number of photons and the energy of one photon. The hill reflects radiation. The energy that arrives at a square metre surface each second is the intensity of the radiation.

2 1 radio, 2 infrared, 3 information, 4 optical, 5 receiver, 6 AM; 7 analogue; 8 digital; 9 interference, 10 decode; 11 noise

3 1 Radio waves, no damage. 2 Microwaves; heat up cells and damage them, protect by shutting microwave oven door. 3 Microwaves: may heat up cells and damage them in young children; protect children by making them use hands free or texting instead of phoning. 4 X-rays; ionise atoms or molecules and so damage DNA of living cells, which may lead to cancer or cell death; protect by using only when necessary and dentist to be out of the room, or behind lead shield. 5 UV; damages cells, leading to cell death or cancer; protect by covering up with clothes, wearing sunscreen, keeping in the shade. 6 Gamma rays; in nuclear power station; cause cancer and cell death; keep out! 7 Light waves from TV; no damage.

P2 Quickfire

1 Ionising radiations: a, c, e; radiations that cause a heating effect only: b, d, f

2 G, D, B, C, F, A, E

3 a C   **b** O   **c** B
   d O   **e** C   **f** C

4 True statements: b, c
Corrected version of false statement:
a The higher the frequency of an electromagnetic radiation, the more energy is transferred by each photon.

5 Microwaves, radio or TV, radio or TV, absorbed, visible light or infrared, visible light or infrared, absorbed

6 X: it is made up of the greatest amount of stored information.

7 In order, from top of left column: digital signal without noise; analogue signal with noise; analogue signal without noise; digital signal with noise.

8 a Respiration and volcanic activity.
b One from: photosynthesis, dissolving, sedimentation/forming carbonaceous rocks.
c Humans have burned more fossil fuels; forests have been cleared for farmland.
d Methane and water vapour.
e Climate change, meaning some food crops will no longer grow in some places; ice melting and seawater expanding as it warms up, causing rising sea levels and flooding of low lying land; more extreme weather conditions.

9 a Water
b Sunscreen and clothing
c Lead and other dense materials

10 The energy arriving at a square metre of a surface each second

11 Because it reaches an ever-increasing surface area, and because some of the radiation is absorbed by the medium it is travelling through

12 Ozone O_3; oxygen O_2. When an ozone molecule absorbs ultraviolet radiation, the molecule may break down.

13 The principal frequency of the radiation emitted by an object is the frequency that is emitted with the highest intensity. The Sun has a higher principal frequency than the Earth.

14 Higher temperatures cause more convection in the atmosphere, and more evaporation of water from oceans and land.

P2 GCSE-style questions

1 a i Two from: Combustion, respiration, volcanic activity, decomposition
ii Two from: Photosynthesis, dissolving in water, sedimentation/forming carbonaceous rocks
b i Rising sea levels; changing climates
ii Methane, water vapour

2 a Transmitted
b Absorbs; if the intensity of the light that comes out of the brain is less than expected, the brain might be bleeding. This suggests that blood absorbs light, so the intensity of transmitted light decreases.

c   In one second, a different number of photons arrives at each detector.

d   i   One of: X-rays damage living cells and can cause cancer; X-rays will be absorbed by the bone of the skull, so will give no useful information.

    ii   Microwaves have a heating effect, so will heat up brain tissue causing great damage

3   5/6 marks

Answer clearly describes all the trends shown by the graphs, and refers to data from them.
and identifies correlations shown by pairs of graphs.
and indicates that correlations are not necessarily causal. All information in the answer is relevant, clear, organised and presented in a structured and coherent format. Specialist terms are used appropriately. Few, if any, errors in grammar, punctuation and spelling.

3/4 marks

Answer identifies trends shown by some of the graphs, and refers to data from some of them.
and identifies two or three correlations shown by the graphs.
Most of the information is relevant and presented in a structured and coherent format. Specialist terms are usually used correctly. There are occasional errors in grammar, punctuation and spelling.

1/2 marks

Answer indentifies trends shown by some of the graphs, but does not refer to data from them.
or identifies one or two correlations shown by the graph.
and may incorrectly state or imply that the correlations are necessarily causal.
There may be limited use of specialist terms. Errors of grammar, punctuation and spelling prevent communication of the science. Answer includes 1 or 2 points of those listed below.

0 marks

Insufficient or irrelevant science. Answer not worthy of credit.
Relevant points include:

- Graph A shows that average temperature has increased since 1880, with the most rapid increases being since about 1950.
- Graphs B and E show that the concentrations of methane and carbon dioxide in the atmosphere have increased over time.
- Graphs A, B, and E show that here are correlations between average temperature and the concentrations of methane and carbon dioxide.
- The correlation does not prove that increasing concentrations of methane and carbon dioxide are the cause of global warming.
- Graph C shows that sea levels have increased over time.
- Graph D shows that sea pH has decreased over time.
- Graphs A and C show that there is a correlation between average temperature and sea levels.
- The correlation does not prove that increasing average temperatures increases sea levels.
- Graphs B and D show that there is a correlation between carbon dioxide concentration and sea pH. The correlation does not prove that increasing carbon dioxide concentration in the atmosphere causes decreased sea pH.

4   The intensity of the radiation arriving at Helen's phone is less *or* the distance between Helen and the source is greater.

B3 Workout

1   –

2   –

3   a   Stores: atmosphere, fossil fuels; processes: photosynthesis, combustion, respiration, eating, dying, decomposing

    b

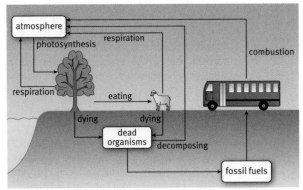

4   Animal Kingdom, Animal Kingdom, species, similar, characteristics

B3 Quickfire

1   a   N   b   L   c   N   d   L

2   Variation – differences between organisms
Mutations – changes to genes
Habitat – the place where an organism lives
Environment – everything around an organism, including air, water, and other living things

3   Small, photosynthesis, chemicals, energy, moving, warm, heat, waste, dead, materials

4   True statements: **c, d**
Corrected versions of false statements:
a Life on Earth began about 3500 million years ago.
b Mutated genes in sex cells can be passed to offspring.

5   Thick fur provides insulation to help keep them warm; white colour is camouflage so their prey cannot see them easily; good swimmers mean they can move from place to place.

6   a   Termite, kangaroo, wombat
    b   Grass, eucalyptus tree
    c   Honeyeater bird, termite, kangaroo, wombat
    d   The wombat population might increase since there would be less competition for its food (grass).
    e   The honeyeater bird population would decrease.
    f   The wombat population might increase since dingoes are its predator.

7   14%

8   There are changes in the environment to which a species cannot adapt; a new species arrives that competes with, eats, or causes disease of the species; another species in its food web becomes extinct.

9   Darwin's theory fits in with advances in understanding of genetics; there is no evidence or mechanism for Lamarck's ideas about the inheritance of acquired characteristics.

10 Interdependence means that species in a habitat rely on each other for food and other needs.

11 A detritivore is an organism that feeds on dead organisms and waste.

12 Decay – breaks down proteins
Nitrogen fixation – forms nitrates from nitrogen
Excretion – removes waste from an organism
Denitrification – breaks down nitrates to form nitrogen

B3 GCSE-style questions

1 a i Antarctic whelk *or* brittlestar *or* Trematomus bernacchii fish
    ii Their populations will decrease.
  b Environmental conditions change; a new species that is a predator of the brittlestar is introduced to Antarctica.

2 5/6 marks
Answer clearly explains how energy is transferred from one organism to another in a food chain
and explains in detail what happens to the energy at each stage of the food chain, giving at least **three** examples.
All information in the answer is relevant, clear, organised and presented in a structured and coherent format. Specialist terms are used appropriately. Few, if any, errors in grammar, punctuation and spelling.

3/4 marks
Answer explains how energy is transferred from one organism to another in a food chain
and explains what happens to the energy at each stage of the food chain, giving at least **one** example.
Most of the information is relevant and presented in a structured and coherent format. Specialist terms are usually used correctly. There are occasional errors in grammar, punctuation and spelling.

1/2 marks
Answer explains how energy is transferred from one organism to another in a food chain
or explains what happens to the energy at each stage of the food chain, giving at least **one** example.
AND the explanation lacks detail/clarity.
There may be limited use of specialist terms. Errors of grammar, punctuation and spelling prevent communication of the science. Answer includes 1 or 2 points of those listed below.

0 marks
Insufficient or irrelevant science. Answer not worthy of credit.
Relevant points include:
- Energy is transferred when animals eat other organisms.
- Energy is transferred when decay organisms eat dead organisms and waste materials.
- A small percentage of energy is passed on because the rest of the energy
  - is used for life processes (eg moving)
  - escapes to the surroundings as heat
  - is excreted and passed on to decomposers
  - cannot be eaten and is passed on to decomposers

3 a Studying fossils; analysing the DNA of modern cats, lions, and other species of the cat family.
  b i Selection
    ii C, B, D, A

  c i 6.7 million years ago
    ii Fishing cat
    iii Environmental, isolation, natural, selection

C3 Workout

1
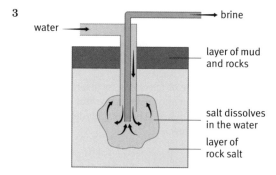

2 Fossils – different animals lived at different times, so fossils tell us about the ages of the rocks they are in.
Sand grains – comparing sand grains in deserts and rivers to sand grains in sandstones tells us what sort of sand formed the sandstone.
Ripples – the shapes of ripples in rocks give clues about whether the sand was made from river bed sand or desert sand. Shell fragments in limestone tell us about the conditions when the rock formed.

3

4 1 soap; 2 oxidised; 3 hydroxide; 4 limestone; 5 solution; 6 magnetic; 7 tectonic; 8 hydrogen; 9 flavouring; 10 polymer; 11 chlorine; 12 fossils; 13 distances; 14 pressure

C3 Quickfire

1 a R   b P   c P
  d R   e R

2 Chlorine – to make hydrochloric acid and to make bleach
Sodium hydroxide – to make soap and to make bleach
Hydrogen – as a fuel and to make hydrochloric acid
Sodium chloride – to de-ice roads, to preserve food

3 Polymer, long, carbon, window frames, wire insulation, plasticiser; small, toys

4 Materials, product, energy, chemicals, discarded, energy

5 Sedimentation – with compression, formed limestone when dead sea creatures sank
Erosion – formed sand, which deposited in layers to form sandstone
Evaporation – formed rock salt when a sea moved inland
Mountain building – pushed coal nearer the surface

6 a Tuberculosis, pneumonia (but very similar in both years), typhoid

    b No; some other factor could have caused the decrease in number of deaths from these diseases.

7 They do not break down in the environment; they move long distances in the air and water; they build up in fatty tissues of animals and humans.

8 a Sodium nitrate and water

    b Potassium sulfate and water

    c Potassium chloride, carbon dioxide, and water

    d sodium sulfate, carbon dioxide, and water

    e Potassium chloride and water

    f Sodium nitrate, carbon dioxide, and water

9 a Sodium hydroxide + nitric acid $\longrightarrow$ sodium nitrate + water

    b Potassium hydroxide + sulfuric acid $\longrightarrow$ potassium sulfate + water

    c Potassium carbonate + hydrochloric acid $\longrightarrow$ potassium chloride + carbon dioxide + water

    d Sodium carbonate + sulfuric acid $\longrightarrow$ sodium sulfate + carbon dioxide + water

    e Potassium hydroxide + hydrochloric acid $\longrightarrow$ potassium chloride + water

    f Sodium carbonate + nitric acid $\longrightarrow$ sodium nitrate + carbon dioxide + water

C3 GCSE-style questions

1 a Putting together the computer components in its plastic case – manufacturers make the computer
Recycling the computer components – people throw away the computer
Extracting oil from wells beneath the sea – materials are produced
Dismantling the computer – people throw away the computer
Making plastics from oil – materials are produced

    b i 1285 kg

       ii 5045 kg

      iii Two points from: Making the computer requires inputs of materials and energy, and results in the emissions of greenhouse gases. The fewer new computers that are made in a given year, the smaller these inputs and emissions. When a computer is discarded, it is dismantled and the components recycled. These processes use energy. The fewer computers that are discarded in a given year, the smaller the energy input for these processes.

    c i Benefit to the environment: extracting metals from rocks leads to larger amounts of waste than using recycled precious metals. Benefit to people: companies that recycle computers can make money by selling their precious metals. *Many other answers are acceptable here.*

       ii Risk: inhaling beryllium dust, which is toxic and which may cause cancer. People still dismantle computers because they can sell the valuable metals they contain.

2 5/6 marks
Answer clearly describes each method of manufacturing alkalis
and clearly describes the advantages and disadvantages of each method.

All information in the answer is relevant, clear, organised and presented in a structured and coherent format. Specialist terms are used appropriately. Few, if any, errors in grammar, punctuation and spelling.

3/4 marks
Answer describes each method of manufacturing alkalis **and** gives an incomplete account of the advantages and disadvantages of some of the methods
or gives a complete account of the advantages and disadvantages of the methods, but this lacks detail/clarity. Most of the information is relevant and presented in a structured and coherent format. Specialist terms are usually used correctly. There are occasional errors in grammar, punctuation and spelling.

1/2 marks
Answer describes one or two methods of manufacturing alkalis
and gives an advantage and/or disadvantage of one of these methods.
and the explanation lacks detail/clarity.
There may be limited use of specialist terms. Errors of grammar, punctuation and spelling prevent communication of the science. Answer includes 1 or 2 points of those listed below.

0 marks
Insufficient or irrelevant science. Answer not worthy of credit.
Relevant points include:
- alkalis were first made from burnt wood and stale urine...
- ...advantages – materials readily available
- ...disadvantages – the materials were not available in large enough quantities by the time of the industrial revolution
- alkalis were then manufactured from sodium chloride, coal, and limestone...
- ...advantages – could be manufactured in larger quantities
- ...disadvantages – produced pollutants, including hydrogen chloride gas and hydrogen sulfide gas from solid waste produced in the process
- electrolysis of brine...
- ...advantages – can be produced in large quantities and only one raw material needed. The process produces other useful products
- ...disadvantages – process requires huge amounts of electrical energy

3 a Salt raises blood pressure, which increases the risk of heart attacks and strokes.

    b i Canada

       ii People in different countries might have different tastes; there may be stricter regulations in some countries than others.

      iii 6.4 g

      iv This mass of salt is greater than the maximum daily UK recommended amount of salt for a 16-year-old. Pedro should aim to cut down his salt intake, and not eat two burgers in one day.

4 a Copper chloride, carbon dioxide, water

    b Sodium nitrate and water

    c Potassium sulfate and water

Answers

P3 Workout

1 1 B or C or G; 2 A; 3 D; 4 F; 5 B or C or G; 6 B or C or G; 7 E

2 –

3 Person on left: A, C, D, E; person on right: B, D, E, F

P3 Quickfire

1 b, c, d, e, f

2 Voltage – volt; energy – kilowatt-hour, joule; current – amp; time – hour, second; power – watt

3

	Biofuels	Gas	Solar
It is a primary energy source.	√	√	√
It is a renewable energy source.	√		√
When electricity is generated from it, CO_2 is produced.	√	√	
The generation of electricity from this source is weather dependent.			√
When electricity is generated from it, no waste is produced.			√

4 A, F, B, D, C, G, E

5

Device	Power rating (W)	Power rating (kW)	Time it is on for	Energy transferred (kWh)
computer	250	0.250	2 hour	0.5
kettle	1800	1.800	3 min	0.09
toaster	1200	1.200	5 min	0.1
phone charger	20	0.02	2 hour	0.04

6 Switch off appliances, use energy efficient appliances, walk instead of going by car. *Other points are acceptable here.*

7 Provide more efficient public transport, generating electricity more efficiently, making laws about energy efficiency of new homes and workplaces

8 a 23.75p **b** 10p

9 a 17% **b** 27 kJ

10 Because energy is conserved, so the total amount of energy must remain the same.

11 The power of a device or appliance is the rate at which it transfers energy.

12 A country needs a mix of energy sources to ensure continuity of supply.

P3 GCSE-style questions

1 a i 120 × 2 MW gains I mark 240 gains the second mark.
   ii 5760 MWh 240 MW × 24h gains I mark. 5760 MWh gains the seond mark.
  b 1 163 077 people
  c i To follow the Sun so as to maximise the energy that it receives
   ii 15%

d There may be no more places in which hydroelectric power stations can be built; it is wise to have a mix of energy sources to ensure continuity of supply.
e i The energy is renewable (or any other sensible answer).
  ii They were worried about hazards to shipping, or possible damage to wildlife.

2 5/6 marks
Answer clearly identifies several advantages **and** disadvantages of replacing fossil fuels with biofuels **and** comes to a judgement about which is the better choice **and** gives clear reasons for the judgement, linked to the advantages and disadvantages given.
All information in the answer is relevant, clear, organised and presented in a structured and coherent format. Specialist terms are used appropriately. Few, if any, errors in grammar, punctuation and spelling.

3/4 marks
Answer identifies some advantages **and** disadvantages of replacing fossil fuels with biofuels **and** gives to a judgement about which is the better choice. **but** does not give reasons for the judgement
Most of the information is relevant and presented in a structured and coherent format. Specialist terms are usually used correctly. There are occasional errors in grammar, punctuation and spelling.

1/2 marks
Answer identifies a few advantages **or** disadvantages of replacing fossil fuels with biofuels **or** gives a judgement about which is the better choice. **but** does not give reasons for the judgement
There may be limited use of specialist terms. Errors of grammar, punctuation and spelling prevent communication of the science. Answer includes 1 or 2 points of those listed below.

0 marks
Insufficient or irrelevant science. Answer not worthy of credit.
Relevant points include:
- Fossil fuels and biofuels produce carbon dioxide (a greenhouse gas) when they burn
- Fossil fuels and biofuels may produce other gaseous pollutants, and particulates, when they burn
- Fossil fuels are not renewable
- Biofuels are renewable
- Plants from which biofuels are made take in carbon dioxide from the atmosphere as they grow
- Plants from which biofuels are made may be grown on land that could be used to grow food
- An evaluation referring to the points above – is the government's idea to replace fossil fuels with biofuels a good one?

3 a A furnace; B steam; C generator; D water; E turbine; F transformer
  b 25%
  c It produces huge amounts of carbon dioxide
  d For: the nuclear power station does not produce carbon dioxide when it is being used. Against: the nuclear power station relies on fuel that may need to be imported; there are radiation hazards associated with nuclear power stations. *Other points are acceptable here.*

Ideas about science 1 Workout

1. 1 data, 2 range, 3 outlier, 4 repeatable, 5 melting point, 6 inaccurate, 7 mean, 8 higher, 9 true 10 repeat, 11 lowest, 12 solid, 13 opinions, 14 no, 15 silver

2. The temperature in the main part of the room is different from the temperature behind the curtain; the thermometer may be inaccurate; he may read the thermometer incorrectly.

3. a A   b B   c D   d A and C

Ideas about science 1 GCSE-style questions

1. a i 5
       ii There is no specific reason to doubt its accuracy.
    b Range = 1.2 to 1.6 g; mean = 1.4 g
    c The mean for restaurant B is outside the range of the mean for restaurant A.
    d The data for restaurant B is reproducible.

2. b i Outlier = 11
       ii Student R did not use the measuring equipment properly *or* student R's measuring equipment was faulty.
    c i Mean = 27 $\mu g/m^3$
       ii Range = 21 to 34 $\mu g/m^3$

3. a Wind direction varied; a nearby coal-fired power station was running on some days, but not on others; one student used the measuring equipment incorrectly; (1 mark if all three correct answer are given).
    b The percentage of damaged sperm in samples taken from men at regular intervals throughout the six months.

4. 5/6 marks
    Answer gives correct values of the mean and range for each car
    and points out that the mean for car A is within the range of car B, and vice versa
    and clearly states that this means there is no real difference between the carbon dioxide emissions for the two cars.
    All information in the answer is relevant, clear, organised and presented in a structured and coherent format. Specialist terms are used appropriately. Few, if any, errors in grammar, punctuation and spelling.

    3/4 marks
    Answer correctly gives the values of the means for both cars **or** the ranges for both cars **or** one of each
    and points out that the mean for car A is within the range of car B **or** the mean for car B is within the range of car A.
    or states that there is no real difference between the carbon dioxide emissions for the two cars
    Most of the information is relevant and presented in a structured and coherent format. Specialist terms are usually used correctly. There are occasional errors in grammar, punctuation and spelling.

    1/2 marks
    Answer correctly gives the values of the range for one car **or** the mean for one car
    and states that there is no real difference between the carbon dioxide emissions for the two cars.
    There may be limited use of specialist terms. Errors of grammar, punctuation and spelling prevent communication of the science. Answer includes 1 or 2 points of those listed below.

0 marks
Insufficient or irrelevant science. Answer not worthy of credit.
Relevant points include:
- The mean for car A is 158 g/km
- The mean for car B is 160 g/km
- The range for car A is 153 – 163 g/km
- The range for car B is 156 – 164 g/km
- The mean for car A is within the range of car B, and the mean for car B is within the range of car A
- This means that there is no real difference between the carbon dioxide emissions for the two cars

5. a The concentrations of atmospheric CO_2 in 1990, 2000, and now.
    b The concentrations of both atmospheric CO_2 and of CO_2 dissolved in seawater, in at least two different years.
    c The concentration of atmospheric CO_2 might increase more slowly than the scientist predicted; shellfish might adapt and be able to make shells at a pH lower than they can now; any other sensible suggestions.

Ideas about science 2 Workout

1. A, B, C, E

2. A8 larger, B3 correlation, C6 chance, D4 control, E9 mechanism, F10 random and F7 matched, G2 outcome, H1 factors, I5 causes

Ideas about science 2 GCSE-style questions

1. a Factor: type of shampoo; outcome: percentage of breakage
    b i Person the hair is from, length of hair
       ii To make sure the test is fair
    c There could be some other factor that made the hair that was washed with the anti-break shampoo stronger.

2. a Factors: A, F; outcomes: B, C, E
    b Outcome B: The atmospheric concentration of sulfur dioxide 3000 m above the ground may have changed very little.
    Outcome C: the atmospheric concentration of nitrogen dioxide near the ground over southern England may have changed.
    c 1 – C; 2 – D; 3 – A; 4 – B

3. 5/6 marks
    Answer clearly identifies correlations between the factor and three outcomes
    and points out that the correlations could be causal, or not
    and suggests that the presence of a plausible mechanism linking factor and outcome increases confidence in factor having caused the outcome.
    All information in the answer is relevant, clear, organised and presented in a structured and coherent format. Specialist terms are used appropriately. Few, if any, errors in grammar, punctuation and spelling.

    3/4 marks
    Answer identifies correlations between the factor and two or more outcomes
    and points out that the correlations could be causal, or not
    or suggests that the presence of a plausible mechanism linking factor and outcome increases confidence in factor having caused the outcome
    Most of the information is relevant and presented in a structured and coherent format. Specialist terms are usually used correctly. There are occasional errors in grammar, punctuation and spelling.

Answers

1/2 marks

Answer identifies a correlation between the factor one outcome

or points out that correlations could be causal, or not

There may be limited use of specialist terms. Errors of grammar, punctuation and spelling prevent communication of the science. Answer includes 1 or 2 points of those listed below.

0 marks

Insufficient or irrelevant science. Answer not worthy of credit.

Relevant points include:

- When smoking was banned, pub workers had fewer symptoms of smoke irritation – this is an example of a correlation between a factor (smoking being banned) and an outcome (pub workers having fewer symptoms of smoke irritation)
- When smoking was banned, pub workers' breathing difficulties had decreased by 70% - this is an example of a correlation between a factor (smoking being banned) and an outcome (pub workers' breathing difficulties decreasing)
- when smoking was banned, the mean concentration of carbon monoxide in pub workers' exhaled breath had decreased by 40% - this is an example of a correlation between a factor (smoking being banned) and an outcome (decreased concentration of carbon monoxide in pub workers' exhaled breath)
- For any of the correlations, the outcome could have been caused by the smoking ban. Then there is a causal relationship between the factor and outcome.
- For any of the correlations, the outcome could have been caused by something other than the smoking ban (the factor that changed)
- The scientists could try to work out a plausible mechanism that links the factor and any of the outcomes. This would increase confidence in there being a causal correlation between the factor and the outcome.

4 **a** The smaller the concentration of ozone in the atmosphere, the greater your chance of getting a cataract; there is a correlation between the concentration of ozone in the upper atmosphere and the number of people with cataracts; wearing sunglasses that protect against ultraviolet radiation may reduce your chance of getting a cataract.

   b **i** As large as practically possible

      ii Time people spend outdoors; ethnic origin

Ideas about science 3 Workout

1 1 D; 2 A; 3 E; 4 B; 5 C

2 1 A; 2 E; 3 B; 4 D; 5 C

Ideas about science 3 GCSE-style questions

1 Data: B, C, E, F; explanation: D

2 **5/6 marks**

Answer clearly identifies all the stages of developing a scientific explanation in the article **and** clearly shows how the article exemplifies each stage All information in the answer is relevant, clear, organised and presented in a structured and coherent format. Specialist terms are used appropriately. Few, if any, errors in grammar, punctuation and spelling.

3/4 marks

Answer identifies some of the stages of developing a scientific explanation in the article

and shows how the article exemplifies each of the stages identified

or answer identifies all of the stages of developing a scientific explanation in the article **but** does not show how the article exemplifies each of the stages identified

Most of the information is relevant and presented in a structured and coherent format. Specialist terms are usually used correctly. There are occasional errors in grammar, punctuation and spelling.

1/2 marks

Answer identifies one or two of the stages of developing a scientific explanation in the article.

and shows how the article exemplifies this stage.

There may be limited use of specialist terms. Errors of grammar, punctuation and spelling prevent communication of the science. Answer includes 1 or 2 points of those listed below.

0 marks

Insufficient or irrelevant science. Answer not worthy of credit.

Relevant points include:

- The first paragraph describes data the scientists collected by observation – there were more species of fanged frogs on the small island, and there were no *Platymantis* frogs.
- The second paragraph describes a hypothesis, which accounts for the data and which was developed using both data and creative thought.
- From this hypothesis, the scientists made a prediction – that every type of habitat on the small island would have its own species of fanged frogs.
- The scientists then collected data to test the prediction, by identifying fanged frog species in the different habitat types of the small island
- The scientists prediction was correct, since many habitats had their own species of fanged frog.
- The fact that the prediction was correct increased the scientists' confidence in their explanation (the hypothesis)

3 **a** A: C; B: D; C: D; D: E; E: D

   b The data increase confidence in the explanation; the data agree with the prediction.

4 **a** **i** 1 C and H; 2 A; 3 E and F; 4 D; 5 G and I; 6 B

      ii This does not mean the explanation is correct, since there could be another explanation that also accounts for all the data.

     b It is impossible to predict when the next Earth movement will be.

5 **a** **i** Two from A, B, C, E

      ii D

   b The data would not prove that the explanation is correct; the data would agree with the prediction; the data would increase confidence in the explanation.

6 The data supports the prediction, which is an indication that it would be reasonable to accept the explanation. However, the values for blood pressure change are very similar for all four groups, which is perhaps a reason to be sceptical of the explanation.

Ideas about science 4 Workout

1   E, F, A, D, B, C

2   **a**   C   **b**   X   **c**   X
    d   C   **e**   X

3   **Questions might include the following:**
    Peer review – What is the name of the process by which scientists who are experts in their field critically evaluate a scientific idea before and after publication?
    Scientific conference – What is the name given to a meeting of scientists at which experts give talks and discuss their findings?
    Other scientists get similar results – How might confidence in a scientific claim be increased?
    The [old] explanation has stood the test of time – Why might scientists be reluctant to accept a new explanation for a phenomenon or set of data?
    Scientific journal – What is the name of a peer-reviewed publication in which scientific papers are published?
    A tobacco company employs one scientist... – Suggest why two scientists may come to different conclusions about the same data.
    New data may be inaccurate – Suggest why an accepted scientific explanation is rarely abandoned just because some new data disagree with its predictions.
    Different sponsors have paid for the research – Suggest why two scientists may come to different conclusions about the same data.

Ideas about science 4 GCSE-style questions

1   **a**   Four from A, B, D, F, I, J
    b   C, E, G
    c   H, K

2   **a**   **i**   To check their methods and data for obvious problems, as part of the peer-review process
        ii   So that other scientists can try to reproduce their findings, and so that other scientists can build on their findings and plan further research in the same area
    b   The new data disagreed with predictions from the previous explanation.
    c   Their findings make other scientists more likely to accept the claim of the 2005 scientists.
    d   Wine-making company – just two studies show that moderate drinking does not reduce the risk of heart disease. Many more studies show the opposite. People can continue drinking as usual
        Organisation that persuades people not to drink alcohol – the 2005 study shows that the results of the earlier research could well be wrong. People who drink alcohol are not protecting themselves against heart disease.
        European health organisation – we need more information before we can assess whether the claim of the 2005 research is correct.

3   **a**   •   Different scientists may interpret data differently depending on their expertise.
        •   For example, an expert in early plants and animals may interpret data about fossils of early plants and animals differently to a scientist who is an expert in rocks.
        •   Different scientists may interpret data differently depending on their background or who is paying for them to do the research.

b   Three of:
    •   When they find new data that disagrees with the explanation, they might check the data very carefully, to make sure it is correct.
    •   When they find new data that disagrees with the explanation, they might create a new hypothesis – for example the atmosphere contained high enough levels of oxygen for animals to survive earlier than predicted by the previously accepted explanation.
    •   They might then make a prediction based on this new hypothesis.
    •   They might then collect further data to test this prediction.

4   **a**   So that other scientists can try to reproduce the findings in future; so that other scientists can ask questions about the findings
    b   **i**   The shapes of the continents seemed to fit together like a jigsaw; the rock types of eastern South America are the same as those of western Africa; the fossils of eastern South America are similar to those of western Africa.
        ii   The idea of continents moving was outside their experience; they could not imagine how the continents could move; Wegener was not regarded as a member of the community of geologists.
        iii   Data collected since 1912 support the explanation; data collected since 1912 agree with predictions based on the explanation.

Ideas about science 5 Workout

1   1 harm; 2 chance; 3 advance; 4 ionising; 5 consequences; 6 assess; 7 controversial; 8 statistically; 9 benefit; 10 perceive; 11 acceptable

2   **Sentences might include the following:**
    •   People's perceptions of the size of a particular risk may be different from the statistically estimated risk.
    •   The perceived risk of an unfamiliar activity is often greater than the perceived risk of a more familiar activity.
    •   Governments have to assess what level of risk is acceptable in a particular situation. This decision may be controversial.

Ideas about science 5 GCSE questions

1   **a**   Zion and Junaid
    b   Zion, Junaid and Sarah
    c   Catherine

2   **a**   Wear goggles; use the sunbed for a maximum of 15 minutes; do not use the sunbed if you have lots of moles or freckles
    b   **i**   Having a tan makes them feel more confident.
        ii   Statistically calculated risk: B; perceived risk: C
    c   Points that may be included:
        •   Using sunbeds benefits people by making them feel more confident.
        •   Using sunbeds increases the risk of developing skin cancer.
        •   On balance, the danger from the increased risk of skin cancer is more important than the benefits of a tan, so the MP wants to ban sunbeds.

3   **a**   Greenhouse gas emissions decreased.
    b   Chances, consequences

4 a It makes some users feel happy for up to three hours; peer pressure

   b He has chosen to take the drug himself; he perceives the risks as being short-term only.

   c Its use only became widespread in 2007.

   d i blue fingers.

      ii Sweating and headache (study A); agitation (study B)

   e The government considers the risks of taking the drug are too high to allow.

5 a 400 g

   b i The amount of salt in the bread and spread is $(1.5 \times 0.75) + (0.1 \times 1.4) = 1.265$ g
      The amount of salt in the rice flakes and milk is $(1.2 \times 0.5) + (0.04 \times 2) = 0.68$ g
      So Oliver should have the rice flakes and milk.

      ii The oats and milk both have tiny amounts of salt in them.

   c Pressure from health organisations and the government have persuaded manufacturers to reduce the amounts of salt in their products.

   d The government may not want to upset the food industry; the government may believe it is up to people to make their own decisions about whether or not to eat salty food.

Ideas about Science 6 Workout

1 Ticks in boxes next to statements B, C, E, F, H, K

2 Value, unintended, quality, environment, weigh, benefits

3 Words: benefits, costs, sustainable, regulations, ethical, values, questions, technically, feasible, majority, science, views

4 **Notes might include the following:**
   - Title: ethical issues in science
   - Most important points: some questions, including ethical ones, cannot be addressed using a scientific approach; ethics is a set of principles that may show what decision to make in a particular situation.
   - Other information: an example of an ethical issue is whether or not to use embryonic stem cells to treat disease; there are different types of ethical arguments, including 'the right decision is the one that gives the best outcome for the greatest number of people' and 'some actions are always right or wrong, whatever the consequences'

Ideas about science 6 GCSE-style questions

1 a i Ian, Kris

      ii Two from: Grace, Harry, Ian

      iii Jasmine

   b Making sure used fuel rods are disposed of safely; regularly checking storage sites where low-level and intermediate radioactive waste are stored.

2 a Agree: Marcus, Nikki; disagree: Kirsty, Oliver, Linda

   b Scientific approach: does the technique damage embryos? Do embryos that have been tested grow properly? Is PGS necessary – maybe embryos can fix their own genetic defects?
   Values: is PGS ethically acceptable? Is it natural to choose which embryo to implant? Is it right to destroy embryos that are not implanted?

   c Different countries have different laws relating to the ethics of the process; some countries decide not to spend money on treatment.

3 a The energy in the waste is not simply released to the atmosphere as low-grade heat, but is used to provide useful energy. This may reduce the demand for fossil fuels.

   b Costs of transporting the waste to power stations may be high; sorting waste that can be used in this way may be expensive or technically difficult.

4 5/6 marks
   Answer clearly identifies four or more advantages **and** disadvantages of selling the rainforest to the palm oil company
   and comes to a judgement about which is the better choice
   and gives clear reasons for the judgement, linked to the advantages and disadvantages given.
   All information in the answer is relevant, clear, organised and presented in a structured and coherent format. Specialist terms are used appropriately. Few, if any, errors in grammar, punctuation and spelling.

   3/4 marks
   Answer identifies two or three advantages **and** disadvantages of selling the rainforest to the palm oil company
   and gives to a judgement about which is the better choice.
   but does not give reasons for the judgement
   Most of the information is relevant and presented in a structured and coherent format. Specialist terms are usually used correctly. There are occasional errors in grammar, punctuation and spelling.

   1/2 marks
   Answer identifies one or two advantages **or** disadvantages of selling the rainforest to the palm oil company
   or gives a judgement about which is the better choice.
   but does not give reasons for the judgement
   There may be limited use of specialist terms. Errors of grammar, punctuation and spelling prevent communication of the science. Answer includes 1 or 2 points of those listed below.

   0 marks
   Insufficient or irrelevant science. Answer not worthy of credit.
   Relevant points include:
   - benefit – will gain financially
   - cost – forest will not be available for future generations to live in
   - cost – amount of carbon dioxide in the atmosphere will increase
   - cost – loss of biodiversity
   - benefit – burning palm oil to produce electricity will reduce the demand for fossil fuels
   - reasoned decision referring to costs and benefits

5 a There are risks associated with the side effects of all vaccines.

   b A big proportion of the population – or perhaps the whole population – would be protected from mumps, measles, and rubella if the MMR vaccine was compulsory.

Index

Index

Index